PRACTICAL
MUSICAL E

Other Titles of Interest

PRACTICAL ELECTRONIC
MUSICAL EFFECTS UNITS

by

R. A. PENFOLD

**BERNARD BABANI (publishing) LTD
THE GRAMPIANS
SHEPHERDS BUSH ROAD
LONDON W6 7NF
ENGLAND**

Please Note

Although every care has been taken with the production of this book to ensure that any projects, designs, modifications and/or programs, etc., contained herewith, operate in a correct and safe manner and also that any components specified are normally available in Great Britain, the Publishers do not accept responsibility in any way for the failure, including fault in design, of any project, design, modification or program to work correctly, or to cause damage to any other equipment that it may be connected to or used in conjunction with, or in respect of any other damage or injury that may be so caused, nor do the Publishers accept responsibility in any way for the failure to obtain specified components.

Notice is also given that if equipment that is still under warranty is modified in any way or used or connected with home-built equipment then that warranty may be void.

© 1994 BERNARD BABANI (publishing) LTD

First Published — August 1994

British Library Cataloguing in Publication Data
Penfold, R. A.
    Practical electronic musical effects units
    I. Title
    786.74

ISBN 0 85934 368 5

Printed and Bound in Great Britain by Cox & Wyman Ltd, Reading

Preface

I am not sure how long electronic musical effects units have been in existence, but I would guess that the first effects unit arrived on the music scene soon after the first electric guitar. Using electronic gadgets to increase the range of sounds available from electric guitars and electronic instruments has certainly been popular for at least the last 25 years or so. There were apparently a few effects units back in the valve era, and there have even been effects units that were largely mechanical devices. Do-it-yourself add-ons for electric guitars and electronic instruments have a long pedigree as well. Many effects units can be home constructed for far less than the cost of a ready-made equivalent. The do-it-yourself approach also provides access to a range of effects units that have no true commercial equivalents.

This book provides sixteen circuits for musical effects units, including old favourites such as distortion, compression, and waa-waa units, and the more unusual such as an envelope modifier and a split phase tremolo unit. The circuits cover a range of complexities, but none are beyond the capabilities of the average electronics hobbyist. Some are simple enough for beginners to tackle (the soft and hard distortion units, and the waa-waa pedal for example). Where appropriate, notes on any awkward aspects of construction are provided, as are notes on setting up and using the devices. No test equipment is needed in order to get any of the circuits adjusted correctly. All the circuits are based on inexpensive components that are readily available.

R. A. Penfold

Contents

Distortion Units

The distortion effect, or "fuzz" effect as it is also known, is one of the most simple to generate. Indeed, it is almost certainly the most simple of all the musical effects. There are various approaches to producing this effect, but the vast majority of distortion units rely on a clipping circuit of some kind. This produces strong distortion, and is much the same as over-driving an audio amplifier. In fact distortion units of this type are sometimes referred to as "over-drive" units.

There are two basic forms of clipping circuit, which are the "hard" and "soft" varieties. The waveforms of Figure 1 show the difference between the two types. The top waveform is the sinewave input signal, and the middle waveform is this signal after it has been subjected to hard clipping. With this type of clipping the signal rises from zero volts in the usual way, but once the positive threshold voltage is reached the signal voltage increases no further. No matter

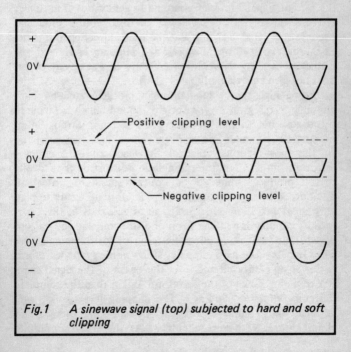

Fig.1   A sinewave signal (top) subjected to hard and soft clipping

1

how positive the input signal goes, the output will not significantly exceed the positive clipping voltage. Once the input voltage has fallen back below the threshold voltage, the output voltage falls back to zero in the normal way. It then starts to increase in the negative direction, but once the negative clipping level is reached the output voltage is unable to rise any further.

Hard clipping clearly produces a severely distorted output signal, even if the input signal only slightly exceeds the clipping levels. This is less than ideal in a musical context, and it gives rise to a number of practical problems. One of these is simply that a hard clipping distortion unit does not give a very controllable effect. Whether the input signal is set well above the clipping threshold, or only marginally above it, the output signal contains strong distortion products. If you try to adjust the degree of clipping so that only the signal peaks are clipped, the result is not a moderate amount of distortion on the output signal. Instead you tend to get an "all or nothing" effect. Initially a large amount of distortion is produced because the signal is strong and the peaks are clipped. As the signal decays it drops beneath the clipping level, and the distortion is abruptly removed. To my ears at any rate, this does not give a particularly musical effect.

Strong high frequency harmonics are generated by hard clipping. This gives a very "bright" sound which is favoured by some, but is not to everyone's liking. Strong intermodulation products are also generated, and this gives rise to the most serious practical drawback of hard clipping distortion units. The intermodulation distortion is so strong that it produces some very discordant sounds if more than one note at a time is played. It is therefore necessary to play with great precision when using an effects unit of this type.

Soft clipping is a milder form of distortion, and the bottom waveform of Figure 1 shows the result of soft clipping a sinewave signal. Like hard clipping, at low voltages the waveform is not significantly altered. At the peaks of the signal there is a rounding down of the waveform, rather than the complete flattening of hard clipping. The clipping level is not well defined, and I suppose that strictly speaking there is no clipping level with soft clipping. As the signal amplitude increases, the gain is steadily reduced. Increases in the signal amplitude always produce some increase in the output level though, albeit very small increases at high input voltages where the clipping is at its hardest.

It is easy to underestimate the differences in the sounds produced by hard and soft clipping. Looking at the clipped waveforms there may not seem to be too much difference between the two. The important difference is the sharp angles in the hard clipping waveform, and the lack of them in the soft clipped one. Soft clipping generates strong lower harmonics, but only weak high frequency harmonics. It gives a much less "bright" but more "full bodied" sound. To my ears, the soft distortion effect is much more musical than the hard distortion variety.

Although the hard distortion effect was popular some years ago, recently there has been increased interest in the more traditional ("Hendrix") distortion effect, which is a soft distortion type. This is also known as the "valve" or "tube" distortion sound, because it is soft clipping that occurs when a valve amplifier is over-driven. There is a strong point in favour of soft distortion in that it generates relatively little intermodulation distortion. This makes it possible to play two or more notes at once without the discordant sounds that occur with hard clipping.

1. Hard Distortion Unit

Both types of distortion effect are normally generated using an operational amplifier clipping circuit. Figure 2 shows the circuit diagram for a hard distortion unit. IC1 is used in what is almost a standard non-inverting amplifier. R1 and R2 bias the non-inverting input to about half the supply potential, and set the input impedance of the circuit at about 50k. This should give good results with any normal guitar pick-up. R3, R4, and VR1 act as the negative feedback network. The voltage gain of the circuit can be varied from 11 times with VR1 at minimum value to 111 times with VR1 set for maximum resistance.

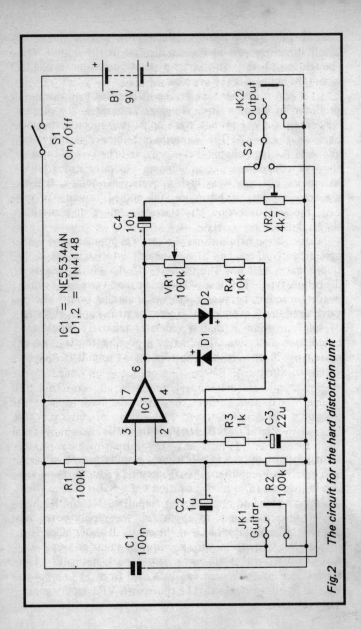

Fig.2   The circuit for the hard distortion unit

4

D1 and D2 are connected in parallel with VR1 and R4, and also form part of the negative feedback circuit. These are silicon diodes, and as such they only begin to conduct significantly once they are forward biased by about 0.6 volts. This means that they have no significant effect on the circuit with peak-to-peak output voltages of less than about 1.2 volts (i.e. plus and minus 0.6 volts). The diodes are brought into conduction when the output level exceeds 1.2 volts peak-to-peak, but only on the signal peaks where the plus and minus 0.6 volt levels are exceeded.

Although a silicon diode has a very high resistance below its forward threshold voltage (typically many megohms), its resistance falls very rapidly above the conduction threshold voltage. With a forward bias of only 0.65 volts or so the resistance might be no more than a few ohms. Thus, as the output voltage tries to go beyond 1.2 volts peak-to-peak, the extra feedback through the diodes reduces the closed loop voltage gain of IC1, and prevents a significant increase in the output voltage. This gives a clipped output signal, and due to the abrupt switch-on characteristic of the silicon diodes it is hard clipping that is produced.

As explained previously, with hard clipping it is not really possible to control the strength of the effect. VR1 does give some control over the amount of distortion added to the input signal, but not enough to be of any great practical value. It is needed more to permit the basic gain of the circuit to be adjusted to suit a wide range of guitar pick-ups. The output level from electric guitars varies enormously from one to another. In fact the highest output pick-ups produce at least ten times the output voltage available from low output types. In general, the higher the cost of a pick-up, the greater its output level.

Adjustment of VR1 should permit good results to be obtained using any normal guitar pick-up(s). For the best results VR1 should be set for the lowest gain (lowest resistance) that gives a properly distorted signal, even once notes have decayed somewhat. Setting a higher level of gain will probably still give good results, but the background noise level will be higher than is really necessary. Also, the more gain that is added into the signal chain, the greater the risk of problems with feedback and "hum". Bear in mind that a fair amount of extra gain is involved even when the unit is used with VR1 at minimum resistance. With any conventional distortion unit added into the system it is always necessary to take extra care to avoid problems with feedback, "hum", and general noise.

The NE5534AN specified for IC1 is a very low noise and distortion bipolar operational amplifier. The low distortion performance of this device is obviously of no practical importance in the current application, but its low noise level does help to keep the background "hiss" level to a minimum. Although devices such as the NE5534AN were once many times more expensive than "ordinary" operational amplifiers such as the Bifet LF351N, the difference in cost is quite small these days. Although the circuit will work quite well using an LF351N, TL071CP, etc., for IC1, the slightly higher cost of the NE5534AN is probably well justified, especially if the unit is used with a low output guitar pick-up. The background noise level is about ten times higher using an LF361N for IC1.

VR2 is a variable output attenuator. This is simply set to give approximately the same volume whether the effect unit is switched in, or bypassed using S2. It is not necessary to use any test equipment to make precise measurements when doing this. It is just a matter of setting VR2 by trial and error, checking for differences in volume "by ear". With guitars that have very high output levels it might be necessary to back-off the guitar's volume control and set VR2 for maximum output. In other words, the guitar might have a higher output level than the distortion unit, making it necessary to adjust the guitar to match the distortion unit, rather than vice versa.

S2 provides a very basic form of bypass switching, but it is a method I have always found to be perfectly adequate in practice. It connects the output socket to VR2's wiper in order to switch in the effect, or connects the output socket direct to the input socket in order to bypass the effect. This leaves the guitar connected to the input of the distortion unit even when the effect is bypassed. This is not likely to cause any problems in use, but the full bypass switching shown in Figure 3 can be used if preferred. I would recommend the use

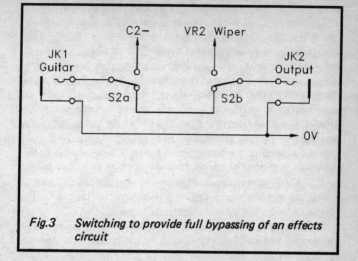

Fig.3 *Switching to provide full bypassing of an effects circuit*

of proper bypass switching if you are in the habit of "daisy-chaining" a number of effects units. Without full bypass switching, if you connected a number of units in series, even with none in use they will all be loading the guitar pick-ups. Incidentally, this method of full bypassing can be applied to any of the effects units featured in this book.

Most users will wish to use the "look no hands" method of switching the effect in and out. This means that S2 must be operated by foot, which in turn means that it should ideally be a heavy duty push-button switch. The usual choice is a heavy duty push-button switch of the successive operation variety. With a switch of this type the effect is switched in the first time the switch is operated, switched out on the next operation, switched in again the third time it is operated, and so on. One slight drawback of this system is that switches of this type tend to be a bit slow in operation, and they are also quite noisy (in terms of the sound they make, not noisy electrically). You may prefer to use a large push-button switch of the non-locking variety. A switch of this type will switch in the effect when it is pressed, and switch it out again when it is released. The only problem with switches of this type is that they are unlikely to be as hard wearing as a heavy-duty type, and might need to be replaced periodically.

Of course, if S2 is a foot operated switch it must be mounted on the top panel of the case where it is accessible, and the case must be a suitably tough type. Diecast aluminium boxes are generally regarded as the best choice as they are extremely strong, and they also provide excellent screening against mains "hum" and other electrical noise. Unfortunately, they are also relatively expensive. Simple folded aluminium boxes offer a good inexpensive alternative. These are nothing like as tough as diecast aluminium boxes, and they have slightly inferior screening properties. However, I have always found them to be perfectly adequate when used as cases for effects units. I would not recommend using plastic cases, some of which are made from a rather brittle type of plastic. Also, plastic cases do not provide electrical screening.

The current consumption of the circuit is only a few milliamps, and a small (PP3 size) 9 volt battery is adequate to supply this. The circuit can be powered from a 9 volt mains power supply unit, but it must be a type which has a low ripple content on its output. In practice this means a good quality type having a stabilised output. Non-stabilised types generally have quite high "hum" levels on their output, and the distortion circuit does not include filtering to deal with this. The circuit for a low noise mains power supply unit is provided in the final section of this book.

Components for Hard Distortion Unit (Fig.2)

Resistors (all 0.25 watt 5% carbon film)
R1	100k
R2	100k
R3	1k
R4	10k

Potentiometer
VR1	100k lin carbon
VR2	4k7 min preset

Capacitors
C1	100n ceramic

8

C2	1μ 50V elect
C3	22μ 16V elect
C4	10μ 25V elect

Semiconductors

IC1	NE5534AN
D1	1N4148
D2	1N4148

Miscellaneous

S1	SPST min toggle
S2	SPDT heavy duty push-button (see text)
JK1	Standard 6.35mm jack socket
JK2	Standard 6.35mm jack socket
B1	9 volt (PP3 size)
	Battery connector
	8 pin DIL IC holder
	Control knob
	Metal case
	Circuit board, wire, solder, etc.

2. Soft Distortion Unit

Figure 4 shows a modified version of the distortion unit which provides soft clipping. All that has been done here is to replace each of the silicon diodes in the original circuit with three germanium diodes connected in series. Germanium and silicon diodes have a very different forward transfer characteristics. The forward resistance of a germanium diode is quite high at very low forward voltages, but nothing like as high as the equivalent figure for a silicon diode. Furthermore, the resistance starts to fall at a much lower voltage, and the transition from the "off" state to the "on" state is far more gradual.

A typical germanium diode begins to conduct more readily at a forward potential of well under 0.1 volts, but does not reach saturation point until the forward voltage has reached almost 0.2 volts. When applied to a clipping amplifier such as

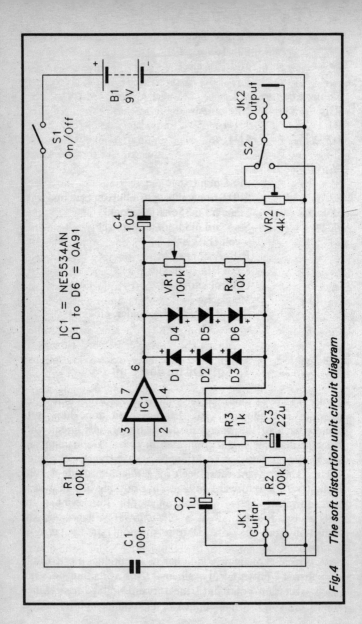

Fig.4   The soft distortion unit circuit diagram

10

the one used in the distortion circuit, a germanium diode therefore gives a more gradual reduction in gain as the input voltage rises. This gives the required soft clipping, and a very good distortion effect. Pairs of three diodes in series are used in order to increase the peak-to-peak output voltage of the circuit to a level which is comparable to that of the hard clipping circuit. Results might be perfectly satisfactory using just one pair of germanium diodes, but it is likely that the output level of the circuit would be inadequate to drive some amplifiers properly.

The notes about constructing and setting up the hard distortion unit apply equally to the soft clipping version, and will not be repeated here. One additional point which should be noted is that germanium diodes are not as hardy as silicon types. In particular, germanium diodes are much more vulnerable to heat damage. D1 to D6 must therefore be soldered into place reasonably quickly, with the iron being applied to each soldered joint for no longer than is really necessary. I have never found it necessary to use a heat-shunt when soldering germanium devices into circuit.

In this version of the unit VR1 provides rather more control over the strength of the distortion effect. However, to a large extent it is still needed to compensate for variations in the output levels from guitar pick-ups. It is worth experimenting with different settings for VR1, and listening carefully to the changes that are produced in the effect. With this soft distortion effect you should find that the effect gradually dies away to nothing on notes that are allowed to fully decay. This contrasts with the hard clipping effect where the distortion tends to end quite abruptly as the signal drops below the rigidly defined clipping level.

When using the unit with low output pick-ups you might find that VR1 must be set at virtually full resistance before the circuit is driven into clipping. Reducing R3 to a value of 470R should boost the gain of the circuit slightly, and make the useful adjustment range of VR1 slightly wider. The input and output of these distortion circuits are in-phase, and they have quite high voltage gains with VR1 set at maximum resistance. It is therefore necessary to take due care to avoid stray feedback when designing the component layouts. With

R3 reduced to 470R it is essential to take just that bit more care with the component layout.

Components for Soft Distortion Unit (Fig.4)

Resistors (all 0.25 watt 5% carbon film)
R1	100k
R2	100k
R3	1k
R4	10k

Potentiometer
VR1	100k lin carbon
VR2	4k7 min preset

Capacitors
C1	100n ceramic
C2	1μ 50V elect
C3	22μ 16V elect
C4	10μ 25V elect

Semiconductors
IC1	NE5534AN
D1 to D6	OA91 (6 off)

Miscellaneous
S1	SPST min toggle
S2	SPDT heavy duty push-button (see text)
JK1	Standard 6.35mm jack socket
JK2	Standard 6.35mm jack socket
B1	9 volt (PP3 size)
	Battery connector
	8 pin DIL IC holder
	Control knob
	Metal case
	Circuit board, wire, solder, etc.

3. "Twangy" Distortion Unit

A conventional distortion unit has a major affect on the processed signal. Apart from adding distortion products, it also changes the input signal's envelope. In other words, it alters the way in which the volume of each note varies. Normally the output from a guitar has a high initial level, but it soon falls away to a much lower level, and then decays at a more gradual rate. The envelope of a signal is one of the all-important parameters that governs its precise character and sound. In the case of a guitar it is the fast attack and quite rapid initial decay that gives the characteristic "twangy" guitar sound.

Clipping the signal from a guitar tends to give an output signal of uniform amplitude right up to the point where the input signal decays away to practically nothing. The fast attack of the input signal is retained, but the rapid fall in amplitude immediately after the attack period is not. This gives a sound which is largely "twang" free! Even with soft clipping, the amount of compression applied to the input signal is such that the original envelope of the signal is largely lost. Of course, for some music it is the excellent sustaining quality of a clipped signal that is required, not the normal "twangy" guitar sound. However, in other cases it is only the added distortion that is needed, and the compression provided by a conventional distortion unit is something that just has to be tolerated.

It is possible to produce a distortion unit that retains the original envelope of the input signal, or something close to it. It requires a rather more complex circuit than an ordinary distortion unit, but a "twangy" distortion unit can still be reasonably simple and inexpensive. The block diagram of Figure 5 shows the arrangement used in this "twangy" distortion unit.

The input signal is applied to a buffer stage, and the signal is then split two ways. The main route is via a soft clipping amplifier, or a hard clipping amplifier can be used here if preferred. The distorted and compressed output signal from the clipping circuit is fed to a v.c.a. (voltage controlled amplifier), and then to the output via a buffer amplifier. The

13

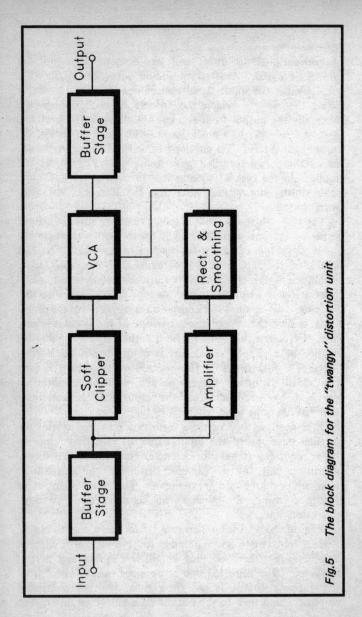

Fig.5   The block diagram for the "twangy" distortion unit

14

amplitude of the output signal is governed by the control voltage fed to the v.c.a. The higher the control voltage to the v.c.a., the higher the amplitude of the output signal. By feeding the v.c.a. with a suitable control voltage, the output signal can be "moulded" into the required envelope shape.

The control voltage is produced by a side chain which first amplifies the input signal. The amplified signal is fed to a rectifier and smoothing circuit. This produces a d.c. output voltage that is roughly proportional to the amplitude of the input signal. Via the v.c.a., this d.c. voltage modulates the output signal to give an output envelope shape that is reasonably close to the envelope shape of the input signal. The output envelope is not identical to the input envelope because a few small errors occur in the amplitude control circuits. However, the match is close enough to give the required "twangy" sound.

The Circuit
Figure 6 shows the circuit for the input buffer and clipping amplifier stages. The circuit for the v.c.a. and other stages is shown in Figure 7. Taking Figure 6 first, the clipping amplifier is based on IC1b. It is basically the same as the clipping amplifier used in the soft distortion unit, and described previously. If hard distortion is required, simply replace D1 to D6 with a pair of silicon diodes connected as in Figure 2. IC1a acts as the input buffer amplifier, and this is a simple non-inverting type which provides an input impedance of 50k. IC1 is an NE5532N, which is a very low noise dual operational amplifier. This provides a similar level of performance to the NE5534AN used in the hard and soft distortion units, although strictly speaking it is not a dual NE5534AN.

A transconductance operational amplifier (IC2) is used as the basis of the v.c.a. Although this is a form of operational amplifier, apart from differential inputs it has little in common with ordinary operational amplifiers such as the 741C and LF351N. A transconductance amplifier is current rather than voltage operated. The output current is controlled by the differential input current. In practical circuits, including the present one, series resistors at the inputs plus a load resistor at the output effectively convert the device to a form

15

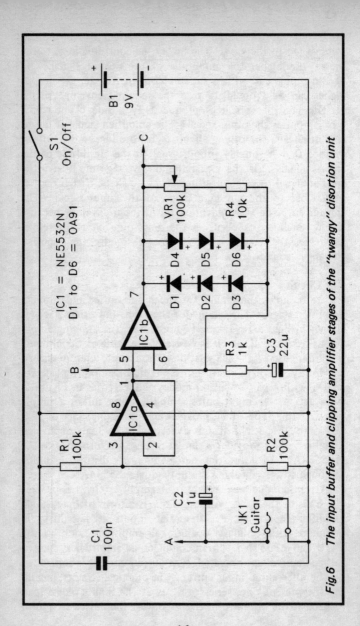

Fig.6   The input buffer and clipping amplifier stages of the "twangy" disortion unit

16

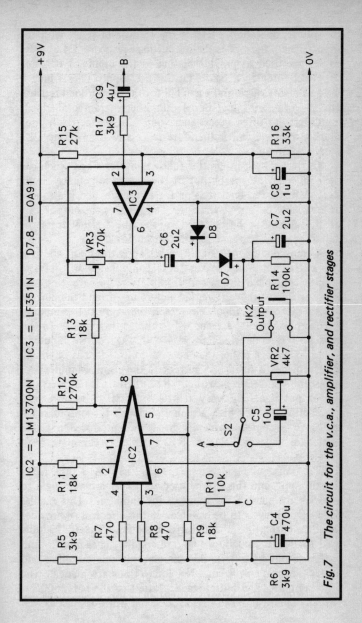

Fig. 7 The circuit for the v.c.a., amplifier, and rectifier stages

17

of voltage operation. R10 is the resistor in series with the input signal, and R9 is the output load resistor. C4 plus R5 to R8 are used to provide biasing to the inputs of IC2, and they also provide a centre-tap on the supply lines which is used as a sort of central earth rail for the output load resistor. Unlike ordinary operational amplifiers, transconductance amplifiers are often used "open loop". IC2 is certainly used in this manner, and it therefore lacks any form of negative feedback circuit.

IC2 has a built-in emitter follower buffer stage which can be connected at the output of the transconductance amplifier. VR2 is the load resistor for this stage, and it also acts as a variable output attenuator. This enables the output level of the circuit to be matched to the direct signal from the guitar, as in the hard and soft distortion units.

A transconductance amplifier has an extra input, and it is this extra input that makes these components so useful in voltage controlled filters and amplifiers. The output current is governed by the differential input current and the current fed to the control input. In effect, the gain of the amplifier is controlled by the current fed to the control input. In this case R13 is connected in series with the control input, so that it is voltage rather than current control that is obtained. R12 provides a small bias current to the control input under quiescent conditions. Without R12 there is a tendency for the output signal to decay a little too fast. Also, when the v.c.a. provides very high attenuation levels the output signal seems to become heavily distorted, and produced a rather unmusical "buzzing" sound. R12 completely eliminates both problems.

The transconductance amplifier in the LM13700N has a fourth input, and this can be used to supply a bias current to linearising diodes at the input of the amplifier. This enables higher signal levels to be handled. In this circuit R10 provides the bias current to the linearising diodes. The LM13700N used for IC2 is actually a dual transconductance amplifier and buffer amplifier, but in this circuit only one amplifier and buffer stage are utilized. No connections are made to the other amplifier and buffer stage. Note that the LM13600N is virtually identical to the LM13700N, and will work just as well in this circuit. Most component retailers now seem to supply the LM13700N, but if you have an LM13600N in the spares box it is perfectly suitable for this circuit.

IC3 is used in the amplifier which drives the smoothing and rectifier circuit. This is an inverting amplifier which has its closed loop voltage gain controlled by VR3. The maximum voltage gain is about 120 times, and this is obtained with VR3 at maximum resistance. The wide range of gains available should enable good results to be obtained using any normal guitar pick-up.

The rectifier and smoothing circuit is a simple half-wave type based on D7 and D8. Germanium diodes are used for D7 and D8 because they have lower forward voltage drops than silicon types, and they therefore give a d.c. output voltage which is a more accurate reflection of the input signal's amplitude. The attack and decay times of the smoothing circuit are kept quite short so that the output envelope accurately follows the envelope of the input signal. On the other hand, the decay time is made sufficiently long to avoid unwanted distortion products on the output signal.

The current consumption of the circuit is about 7 to 8 milliamps. This can be supplied by a PP3 size 9 volt battery, but it would be more economic to use a higher capacity battery (a PP9 or six HP7 size cells in a holder) if the unit is likely to receive a lot of use.

Adjustment

VR1 is simply adjusted to give the best distortion effect. It is advisable to use the lowest resistance that gives good results, as higher resistances will give greater voltage gain, which will in turn encourage problems with feedback and general electrical noise. VR3 should be adjusted before giving VR2 its final setting. Adjusting VR3 is again just a matter of finding the setting that gives what is judged to be the best effect. Setting VR3 too low in value will result in rather a low output level, and generally unimpressive results. Using a value that is too high will give plenty of output signal, but the initial part of the output envelope might be compressed slightly. This will give an output that is slightly lacking in terms of "twangyness".

In between these two extremes there should be a fairly broad range of settings that give good results. Once VR3 has been given a suitable setting, VR2 is adjusted to balance the volume levels obtained with the effect switched in and out.

Components for "Twangy" Distortion Unit (Figs 6 & 7)

Resistors (all 0.25 watt 5% carbon film)

R1	100k
R2	100k
R3	1k
R4	10k
R5	3k9
R6	3k9
R7	470R
R8	470R
R9	18k
R10	10k
R11	18k
R12	270k
R13	18k
R14	100k
R15	27k
R16	33k
R17	3k9

Potentiometer

VR1	100k lin carbon
VR2	4k7 min preset
VR3	470k min preset

Capacitors

C1	100n ceramic
C2	1μ 50V elect
C3	22μ 16V elect
C4	470μ 10V elect
C5	10μ 25V elect
C6	2μ2 50V elect
C7	2μ2 50V elect
C8	1μ 50V elect
C9	4μ7 50V elect

Semiconductors

IC1	NE5532N
IC2	LM13600N or LM13700N
IC3	LF351N
D1 to D8	OA91 (8 off)

Miscellaneous

S1	SPST min toggle
S2	SPDT heavy duty push-button (see text)
JK1	Standard 6.35mm jack socket
JK2	Standard 6.35mm jack socket
B1	9 volt (PP3 size)
	Battery connector
	8 pin DIL IC holder (2 off)
	16 pin DIL IC holder
	Control knob
	Metal case
	Circuit board, wire, solder, etc.

4. Sustain Unit

Sustain units are also known as "compression" units, and the two names simply reflect different ways of viewing the same effect. The sustain name is derived from the fact that a unit of this type effectively extends the guitar's sustain period. Whereas the output from a guitar normally decays fairly rapidly after a string has been plucked, a sustain unit provides a progressive boost in gain which slows down the rate at which the output falls. This boost in gain must be applied dynamically, with no extra gain being applied at the beginning of each note when the guitar's output signal is at high level. As the output level falls, the gain is steadily increased. Of course, the output from the guitar eventually falls to such a low level that it can no longer be sustained, and the signal then decays in the normal way.

The compression name is derived from the fact that this effect compresses the dynamic range of the instrument. If the output from the guitar would normally have fallen by

40dB from its initial level after two seconds, with the aid of a compressor the effective reduction after the same period might be no more than 20dB. In other words, the dynamic range of the signal would have been reduced by 20dB, which is a reduction by a factor of ten.

In practice a sustain unit does not simply enhance the sustain characteristic of a guitar. By ironing out the differences in amplitude between the initial and later parts of the signal, the "twangyness" of the guitar is diminished. If taken to excess it would completely remove the "twangy" characteristic of the sound, giving an effect rather like a distortion unit without the distortion. The sustain effect is probably at its best when the amount of compression used is high enough to give a worthwhile improvement in the effective sustain characteristic of the guitar, but it is not so high as to totally change the character of the sound.

System Operation

The block diagram of Figure 8 shows the general scheme of things used in the compression unit. The main signal path is through a v.c.a. and a buffer stage. The other stages of the unit are used to generate a control voltage for the v.c.a. which gives a suitable compression characteristic. The amplifier driven from the output of the unit is the first stage in this side chain. This feeds into a rectifier and smoothing circuit which produces a positive d.c. signal that is roughly proportional to the strength of the output signal. This signal is fed to the input of an inverting d.c. amplifier, and the output of this stage drives the control input of the v.c.a.

Under quiescent conditions the output from the smoothing circuit is virtually zero, which means that the output from the inverting amplifier is almost equal to the positive supply voltage. This gives a strong control voltage to the v.c.a., which therefore has a modest voltage gain (about four times). If the input level is steadily increased from zero, at first there is little effect on the output voltage from the inverting amplifier. Eventually the input signal is strong enough to overcome various losses through the side chain, and the control voltage to the v.c.a. begins to fall. This tends to reduce the amplitude of the output signal.

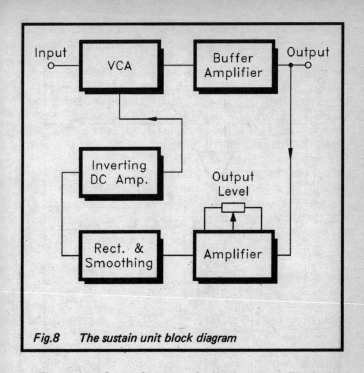

Fig.8   The sustain unit block diagram

This gives a form of negative feedback action. The higher the output level, the lower the control voltage to the v.c.a. becomes. The output level tries to increase, but it is held back by the reducing control voltage fed to the v.c.a. This stabilises the output level, with quite large increases in the input level producing only very small increases in the output level. In the present context it is the effect of the circuit on a steadily diminishing input level that is of interest. As the input level decreases, the output level drops, and the control voltage to the v.c.a. increases. This gives increased gain through the v.c.a. which largely compensates for the drop in input level. This again stabilises the output level, and gives the required sustain effect.

The gain of the amplifier stage is controlled by a variable resistor. The higher the gain of this stage, the lower the input level at which compression commences. This control

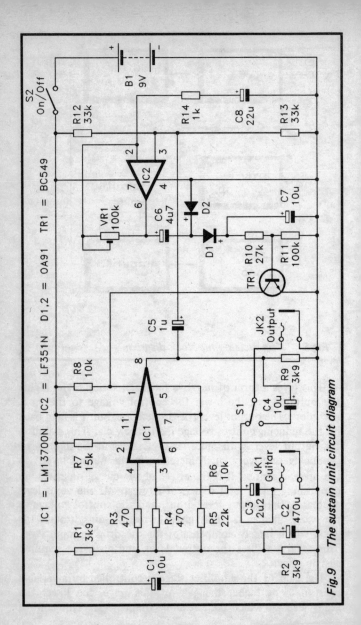

Fig.9   The sustain unit circuit diagram

24

therefore sets the output level of the unit, which is adjusted to match the output level direct from the guitar.

The Circuit

The full circuit diagram for the sustain unit is shown in Figure 9. IC1 is used in the v.c.a., which is essentially the same as the v.c.a. in the "twangy" distortion unit described previously. C5 couples some of IC1's output to the a.c. amplifier stage, which is a non-inverting mode circuit based on IC2. VR1 is the gain control, and it enables the gain to be set at any level up to about 100 times (40dB). This enables the output level to be matched to a wide range of input levels. The unit should therefore work well with high, medium, or low output pick-ups.

D1 and D2 are the diodes in the half-wave rectifier circuit, and C7 is the smoothing capacitor. The attack and decay times of the smoothing circuit are short enough to ensure that the circuit responds rapidly to changes in the input level, but they are long enough to give low distortion levels on the output signal. The d.c. amplifier is a basic common emitter stage based on TR1, and having R8 as its collector load resistor. Although this is a very simple amplifier, it offers good voltage gain and provides excellent results in this application.

The current consumption of the circuit is about 5 milliamps or so. A small (PP3 size) battery is therefore adequate as the power source.

Adjustment

VR1 is simply adjusted by trial and error to obtain what is judged to be the same volume with the effect switched in or out. If VR1 provides adjustment of the output level it is virtually certain that the unit is functioning correctly. However, try temporarily short circuiting the base terminal of TR1 to the 0 volt rail. This should remove the compression, and the output level should then become very much higher. With guitars that have very high output levels it is possible that the unit could become slightly overloaded. One way of correcting this is to power the unit from two batteries wired in series to give an 18 volt supply, but it is probably better just to back-off the guitar's volume control slightly.

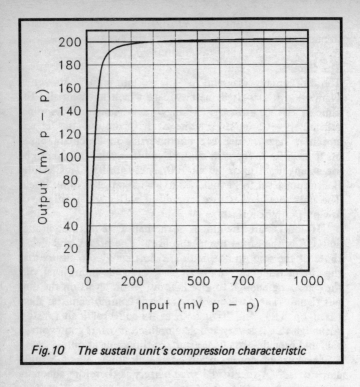

Fig.10   *The sustain unit's compression characteristic*

The graph of Figure 10 shows the compression characteristic obtain from the prototype sustain unit with **VR1** at a
value of about 5k. The voltage gain of the circuit is about four
times (12dB) at low input levels, but the voltage gain reduces
rapidly at input levels of more than about 50 millivolts peak-
to-peak. In fact, raising the input level to one volt peak-to-
peak only takes the output signal marginally above the output
compression threshold of approximately 200 millivolts peak-
to-peak. Only a modest amount of compression is provided
by the circuit using the specified values. If you would prefer
more compression, make R8 a little lower in value and (or)
R5 a little higher in value. Bear in mind that the more compression used, the higher the gain at low signal levels, and the
greater the risk of problems with feedback, "hum", etc.

26

Components for Sustain Unit (Fig.9)

Resistors (all 0.25 watt 5% carbon film)
R1	3k9
R2	3k9
R3	470R
R4	470R
R5	22k
R6	10k
R7	15k
R8	10k
R9	3k9
R10	27k
R11	100k
R12	33k
R13	33k
R14	1k

Potentiometer
| VR1 | 100k min preset |

Capacitors
C1	10μ 25V elect
C2	470μ 10V elect
C3	2μ2 50V elect
C4	10μ 25V elect
C5	1μ 50V elect
C6	4μ7 50V elect
C7	10μ 25V elect
C8	22μ 16V elect

Semiconductors
IC1	LM13700N or LM13600N
IC2	LF351N
TR1	BC549
D1	OA91
D2	OA91

Miscellaneous
| S1 | SPDT heavy-duty push-button |

S2	SPST min toggle
JK1	Standard 6.35mm jack socket
JK2	Standard 6.35mm jack socket
B1	9 volt (PP3 size)
	Battery connector
	8 pin DIL IC holder
	14 pin DIL IC holder
	Metal case
	Circuit board, wire, solder, etc.

5. Parametric Equaliser

Most instruments, including electric guitars, have quite complex output waveforms which contain strong harmonics in addition to the fundamental frequency. This makes it possible to substantially alter the sound of an instrument using various types of filtering. By using high frequency boost for example, the highest harmonics can be boosted to produce a "brighter" sound. A parametric equaliser is a very versatile form of filter which can alter the tone of an instrument in a variety of ways.

A parametric equaliser has three controls, which are the frequency, gain, and Q controls. The basic function of a unit of this type is to boost or attenuate a band of frequencies. With the gain control at a central setting the unit has a flat frequency response regardless of the settings of the other two controls. Backing off the gain control from the middle setting results in the band of frequencies covered by the unit being attenuated. Moving the gain control in the opposite direction results in this band being boosted.

The frequency control enables the centre frequency of the filter to be adjusted. With the Q control at a low setting a wide range of frequencies will be affected by adjustments to the gain control. Using a high Q setting restricts the boost and cut to a narrow band of frequencies. By adjusting the three controls it is therefore possible to obtain boost or cut over a wide or narrow frequency range, and the centre frequency can be practically anywhere within the audio range. Figure 11

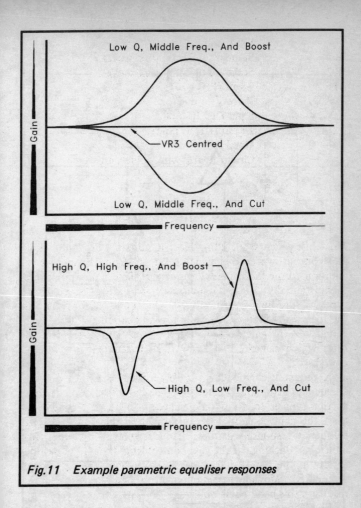

Low Q, Middle Freq., And Boost

VR3 Centred

Low Q, Middle Freq., And Cut

Frequency

High Q, High Freq., And Boost

High Q, Low Freq., And Cut

Frequency

Fig.11   Example parametric equaliser responses

shows the types of filtering obtained at various settings of the three controls.   A unit of this type can be a bit confusing at first, but after a little practical experience you soon learn how to set the required type of filtering.

The Circuit
Figure 12 shows the full circuit diagram for the parametric

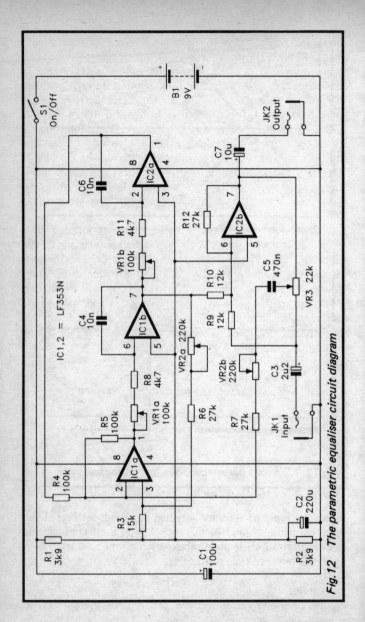

Fig.12 The parametric equaliser circuit diagram

30

equaliser, which has been "borrowed" from "Circuit Source Book 1" (BP321) from the same publisher and author as this book. This is a rather involved form of filter, but it is basically just a variation on a standard state-variable filter. VR1 is the tuning control, and it enables the centre frequency of the filtering to be adjusted from about 150Hz to around 3kHz. VR3 is the boost and cut control. Maximum boost is produced with VR3's wiper at the C3 end of its track — maximum cut is produced with the wiper at the C7 end of the track. The maximum amount of boost and cut available is approximately 15dB. VR2 is the Q control, and this gives maximum Q (minimum bandwidth) when it is set at maximum resistance.

The current consumption of the circuit is about 5 milliamps. The unit can therefore be powered from a small (PP3 size) battery. Construction of this project presents nothing out of the ordinary, but try to keep the wiring to the three controls reasonably short so that stray pick-up is minimised. A little experimentation with the controls will soon reveal the range of effects available. Remember that the unit has little or no effect with the gain control at a roughly central setting.

Components for Parametric Equaliser (Fig.12)

Resistors (all 0.25 watt 5% carbon film)

R1	3k9
R2	3k9
R3	15k
R4	100k
R5	100k
R6	27k
R7	27k
R8	4k7
R9	12k
R10	12k
R11	4k7
R12	27k

Potentiometers
VR1	100k lin dual gang carbon
VR2	220k lin dual gang carbon
VR3	22k lin carbon

Capacitors
C1	100μ 10V elect
C2	220μ 10V elect
C3	2μ2 50V elect
C4	10n polyester 5%
C5	470n polyester
C6	10n polyester 5%
C7	10μ 25V elect

Semiconductors
IC1	LF353N
IC2	LF353N

Miscellaneous
S1	SPST min toggle
JK1	Standard 6.35mm jack socket
JK2	Standard 6.35mm jack socket
B1	9 volt (PP3 size)
	Battery connector
	8 pin DIL IC holder (2 off)
	Control knob (3 off)
	Metal case
	Circuit board, wire, solder, etc.

6. Graphic Equaliser

If you require filtering that is too complex to be handled by a single parametric equaliser, one option is to use two parametric equalisers connected in series. This enables both high frequency and bass boost to be applied, for instance. These days graphic equalisers are probably the more popular choice when complex filtering is required. The more up-market graphic equalisers have about eight to ten level controls, with each one covering a band about one octave wide. With up to about 12dB or so of boost and cut available from each control, units of this type permit very precise doctoring of an audio system's frequency response.

Unfortunately, a full-blown graphic equaliser is a pretty complex and expensive piece of equipment. However, excellent results can be obtained using a more basic unit having four or five level controls, with each one covering about two octaves. The graphic equaliser featured here is a five band type which has approximate centre frequencies of 50Hz, 200Hz, 800Hz, 3kHz, and 12kHz. A little over 12dB of boost and cut is available from each level control. The unit provides very good control over the tone of the instrument connected to its input.

The Circuit

The circuit diagram for the five band graphic equaliser is shown in Figures 13 and 14. IC1a simply operates as an input buffer stage which provides an input impedance of about 50k. This is followed by five stages, one for each band covered. All five stages use the same basic configuration. All five stages are based on inverting mode amplifiers, and they all use R4, R5, and C3 to provide a half supply voltage bias to the non-inverting input.

If we consider the operation of the first stage, which is based on IC1b, this has a centre frequency of 50Hz. For the moment we will ignore C5. With the wiper of VR1 at the top end of its track, C4 shunts R6 at high frequencies and provides high frequency cut. With VR1's wiper at the bottom end of its track, C4 shunts R3 at high frequencies, and provides high frequency boost. Of course, in this application we only require the filtering to be applied to a fairly narrow range of frequencies, not all frequencies above a certain figure. C5 effectively short circuits the track of VR1 at high frequencies, so that R8 shunts R6, but R7 also shunts R3. This leaves the circuit with two identical feedback impedances, and unity voltage gain.

By giving C4 and C5 suitable values the filtering is applied to the appropriate band of frequencies. The filter capacitors in the other stages cover progressively smaller values, so that

33

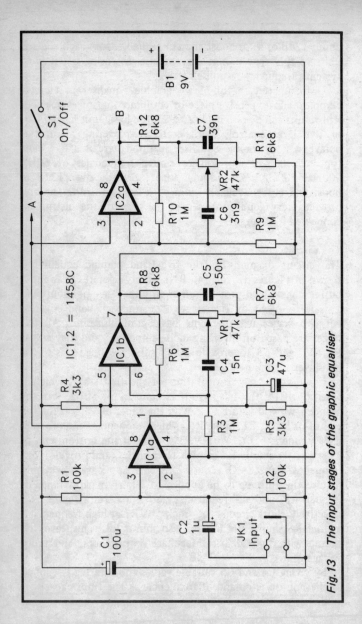

Fig. 13 The input stages of the graphic equaliser

34

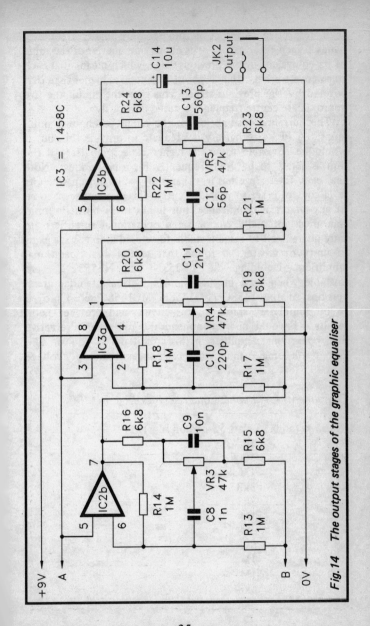

Fig.14   The output stages of the graphic equaliser

35

their respective stages cover progressively higher frequency bands. Each filter capacitor is about one quarter of the value of its equivalent in the previous stage, which means that each stage covers a band that is about two octaves higher than that covered by the previous stage. This gives the circuit the five approximate centre frequencies stated previously.

The current consumption of the circuit is about 6 milli-amps. A PP3 size battery is adequate to provide this, but it would be advisable to use a higher capacity battery if the unit is likely to be used frequently for long periods. Note that each filter stage has less than unity voltage gain when its level control is set to provide "cut". This may not seem to be of any practical significance, but it has to be borne in mind that most internally compensated operational amplifiers are only guaranteed to remain stable for closed loop voltage gains of unity or greater. I found that several dual operational amplifiers, including the LF353N and NE5532N, were unstable when used in this circuit. Several manufacturers' versions of the 1458C (LM1458C, MC1458C, etc.) proved to be completely stable in this circuit, and provided good results. I would not recommend the use of an alternative dual operational amplifier in this circuit unless you are sure that it will remain stable when used at less than unity voltage gain.

Components for Graphic Equaliser (Figs 13 & 14)

Resistors (all 0.25 watt 5% carbon film)

R1	100k
R2	100k
R3	1M
R4	3k3
R5	3k3
R6	1M
R7	6k8
R8	6k8
R9	1M
R10	1M
R11	6k8
R12	6k8

R13	1M
R14	1M
R15	6k8
R16	6k8
R17	1M
R18	1M
R19	6k8
R20	6k8
R21	1M
R22	1M
R23	6k8
R24	6k8

Potentiometers

| VR1 to VR5 | 47k lin carbon (5 off) |

Capacitors

C1	100µ 10V elect
C2	1µ 50V elect
C3	47µ 16V elect
C4	15n polyester
C5	150n polyester
C6	3n9 polyester
C7	39n polyester
C8	1n polyester
C9	10n polyester
C10	220p polystyrene
C11	2n2 polyester
C12	56p polystyrene
C13	560p polystyrene
C14	10µ 25V elect

Semiconductors

IC1	1458C
IC2	1458C
IC3	1458C

Miscellaneous

| S1 | SPST min toggle |
| JK1 | Standard 6.35mm jack socket |

JK2	Standard 6.35mm jack socket
B1	9 volt (PP3 size)
	Battery connector
	8 pin DIL IC holder (3 off)
	Control knob (5 off)
	Metal case
	Circuit board, wire, solder, etc.

7. Treble Booster

A treble booster (also known as a "tone booster") is another
effect that is used to give a guitar a "brighter" sound. All a
device of this type actually does is to provide a certain amount
of high frequency boost to the guitar's output signal. This
boosts the higher frequency components in the signal, and
these will normally be harmonics rather than the fundamental
signal. There is no right or wrong frequency response for a
treble booster, and any circuit which significantly boosts the
higher audio frequencies (above about 2kHz) will provide the
desired effect.

The unit featured here has a control which enables the
amount of boost to be varied to suit individual requirements.
In fact this control can be used to provide high frequency
attenuation if required. Reducing the strength of the higher
frequency harmonics in the signal gives what is either a
"duller" sound, or a more mellow sound, depending on your
musical tastes!

Figure 15 shows the circuit diagram for the treble booster.
This is basically the same as the input stage and first filter
section of the graphic equaliser project described previously.
The value of C4 has been chosen to provide the boost over
the appropriate frequency range. C5 has been given a relatively low value so that it tames the response slightly at the
highest audio frequencies, but the circuit still gives a significant amount of boost right up to 20kHz. It is advisable to
tame the response at very high frequencies, as there could
otherwise be problems with instability and (or) radio frequency breakthrough. S1 provides a simple but effective

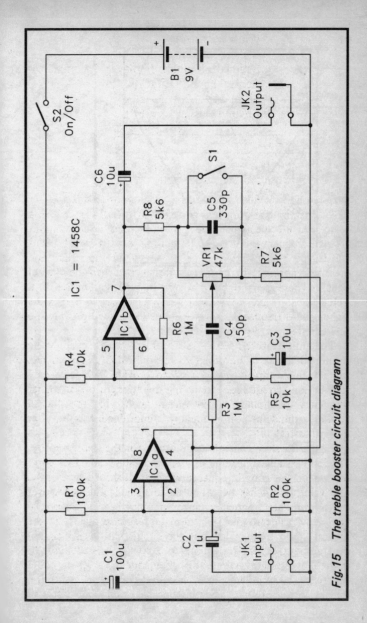

Fig.15 The treble booster circuit diagram

39

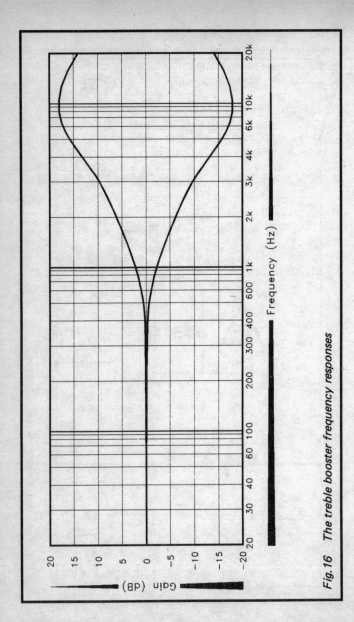

Fig.16   The treble booster frequency responses

40

means of switching out the effect. The feedback circuit is symmetrical when S1 is closed, which gives the circuit a flat frequency response over the audio range.

Figure 16 shows the frequency responses obtained from the prototype with VR1 adjusted for maximum and minimum treble. Up to about 18dB of boost and cut is available at frequencies around 10kHz. The current consumption of the circuit is only about 3 milliamps, and each PP3 size battery will therefore provide many hours of use.

Components for Treble Booster (Fig.15)

Resistors (all 0.25 watt 5% carbon film)
R1	100k
R2	100k
R3	1M
R4	10k
R5	10k
R6	1M
R7	5k6
R8	5k6

Potentiometer
VR1	47k lin carbon

Capacitors
C1	100μ 10V elect
C2	1μ 50V elect
C3	10μ 25V elect
C4	150p polstyrene
C5	330p polystyrene
C6	10μ 25V elect

Semiconductor
IC1	1458C

Miscellaneous
S1	SPST heavy duty push-button
S2	SPST min toggle
JK1	Standard 6.35mm jack socket

JK2	Standard 6.35mm jack socket
B1	9 volt (PP3 size)
	Battery connector
	8 pin DIL IC holder
	Control knob
	Metal case
	Circuit board, wire, solder, etc.

8. Bass Booster

A bass booster, as its name implies, simply provides a certain amount of bass boost. When applied to an electric guitar this gives a more "solid" sound having plenty of "thump". This bass booster design is based on the treble booster unit described in the previous section of this book. Like the treble booster, it can be adjusted to provide boost or cut. Bass cut weakens the fundamental frequency, but leaves the harmonics intact, giving a "thinner" sound.

It is important to realise that a bass booster can have no effect unless you play low notes having their fundamental frequencies within the range of frequencies that are boosted. If you play middle A at 440Hz, the lowest frequency on the output signal will be 440Hz. Boosting frequencies below about 300Hz will clearly have no effect on the sound produced. The situation is different for a treble booster, since the output from an electric guitar contains strong harmonics. Thus, even when low pitched notes are played, they provide high frequency harmonics that can be processed by the treble booster.

The circuit diagram for the bass booster is shown in Figure 17. This is identical to the treble booster circuit apart from the different values for C4 and C5. The value of C4 is chosen to give a boost in the response over the appropriate frequency range, but it gives a relatively small amount of boost at the lowest audio frequencies. A somewhat higher value will extend virtually the full boost down to the lowest audio frequencies. However, in practice this could give problems, such as excessive diaphragm movement in the bass driver of

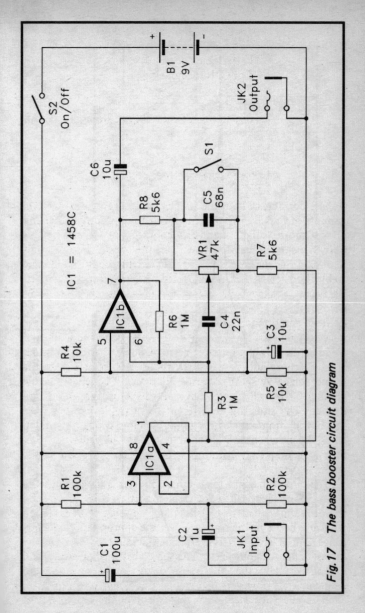

Fig.17   The bass booster circuit diagram

43

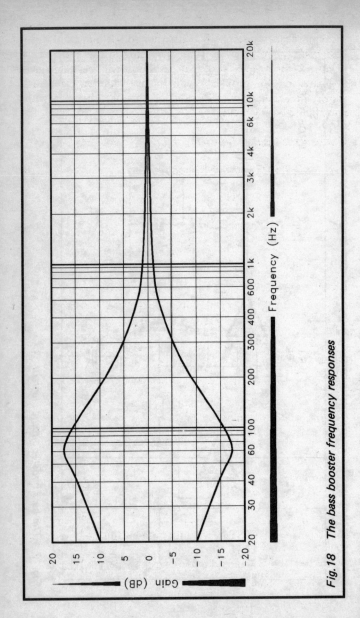

Fig.18   The bass booster frequency responses

44

the loudspeaker system. It is best not to use masses of deep bass boost unless you are sure everything in the system can handle it. Remember also, that bass boost will inevitably give a greater risk of problems with mains "hum". Figure 18 shows the frequency responses of the bass booster with maximum boost and cut.

Components for Bass Booster (Fig.17)

Resistors (all 0.25 watt 5% carbon film)

R1	100k
R2	100k
R3	1M
R4	10k
R5	10k
R6	1M
R7	5k6
R8	5k6

Potentiometer

VR1	47k lin carbon

Capacitors

C1	100μ 10V elect
C2	1μ 50V elect
C3	10μ 25V elect
C4	22n polyester
C5	68n polyester
C6	10μ 25V elect

Semiconductor

IC1	1458C

Miscellaneous

S1	SPST heavy duty push-button
S2	SPST min toggle
JK1	Standard 6.35mm jack socket
JK2	Standard 6.35mm jack socket
B1	9 volt (PP3 size)
	Battery connector

8 pin DIL IC holder
Control knob
Metal case
Circuit board, wire, solder, etc.

9. Guitar Envelope Modifier

This unit changes the sound of an electric guitar by modifying its envelope shape, like the sustain unit described previously. However, the effect it provides is very different to that provided by a sustain unit. It provides a much more radical change to the guitar's sound. A guitar has its characteristic "twangy" sound due to the fast attack time of the envelope, plus its high initial amplitude followed by a rapid decline. This gives an envelope shape of the general type shown in Figure 19 (top). By modifying the envelope it is possible to produce a much slower attack time and to remove the initial transient, as in the lower envelope diagram of Figure 19. This gives a very different sound which is in many ways more like an organ than a guitar. With a very long attack time a rather weird effect is obtained, but the sound produced has plenty of creative possibilities.

Basically all the envelope modifier has to do is provide a high degree of attenuation initially, with the gain of the circuit being steadily restored to normal over a variable delay time. The lower envelope diagram of Figure 19 shows the point at which the gain is restored to unity, and the envelope reverts to normal. The block diagram of Figure 20 shows the general arrangement used in the envelope modifier.

The main signal path is through a v.c.a. and an output buffer amplifier. A side chain is used to generate the control voltage for the v.c.a., and provide the slow build-up in gain at the beginning of each note. The first stage in the side chain is an amplifier, and this is followed by a rectifier and smoothing circuit. The output from the smoothing circuit is a positive d.c. signal which is roughly proportional to the strength of the input signal. The attack and decay times of the smoothing circuit are both quite short, so that this d.c. signal responds to rapid changes in the amplitude of the input signal.

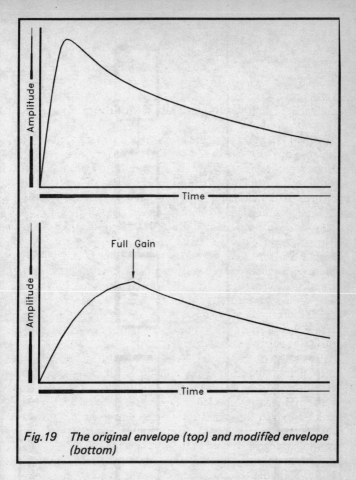

Fig.19 The original envelope (top) and modified envelope (bottom)

The next stage is a voltage detector. Under quiescent conditions this provides a low output level, but in the presence of even a fairly weak input signal the output from the smoothing circuit is high enough to send the output of the voltage detector high. The output of the voltage detector therefore triggers to the high state when a note is played on the guitar. It goes back to the low state if the output from the guitar is allowed to decay to a very low level. It also goes low

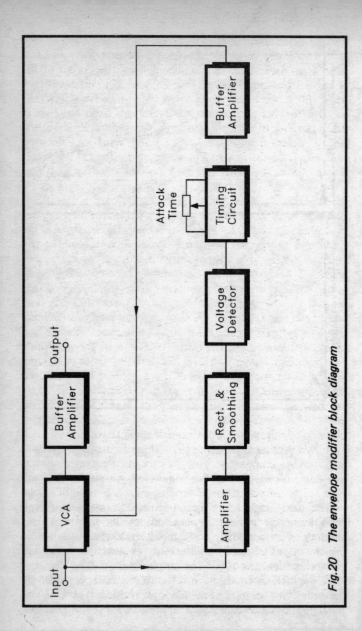

Fig.20   The envelope modifier block diagram

very briefly if another note is played, provided there is at least a very small gap between one note and the next.

A C − R timing circuit is driven from the output of the voltage detector. This provides a slow and variable attack time, but it has a quite rapid decay time. This fast decay time ensures that the circuit always provides a fresh build-up at the beginning of each note, even though the output from the voltage detector only goes low for a very short time between one note and the next. The output from the timing circuit drives the control input of the v.c.a. via a buffer amplifier.

The Circuit

The circuit diagram for the guitar envelope modified appears in Figures 21 and 22. The v.c.a. is basically the same as the one used in the sustain unit (Figure 9), but some of the resistor values have been altered slightly in order to give slightly lower voltage gain at maximum control voltage. The v.c.a. still has a certain amount of voltage gain, and this is needed in order to compensate for the fact that the high amplitude initial part of the envelope is severely attenuated. The voltage gain through the v.c.a. compensates for the loss of volume caused by the initial reduction in the amplitude of the signal, giving what is subjectively about the same volume from the processed and direct signals. The amplifier, smoothing, and rectifier circuits are also basically the same as their equivalents in the sustain unit which was described previously. A few values have been altered in order to give improved performance in the present application.

IC3 is used as the basis of the voltage detector. It operates as a voltage comparator having a reference potential of just over one volt supplied to the non-inverting input by R15 and R16. The output of the smoothing circuit is coupled to the non-inverting input, and the output will trigger to the high state when the output from the smoothing circuit exceeds the reference potential. R17 provides a small amount of positive feedback and hysteresis to ensure that rapid and glitch-free triggering of IC3's output is obtained.

The attack time of the C − R timing circuit is controlled by the time constant of C9 and the series resistance of VR2 and R19. VR2 enables the attack time to be varied. The attack

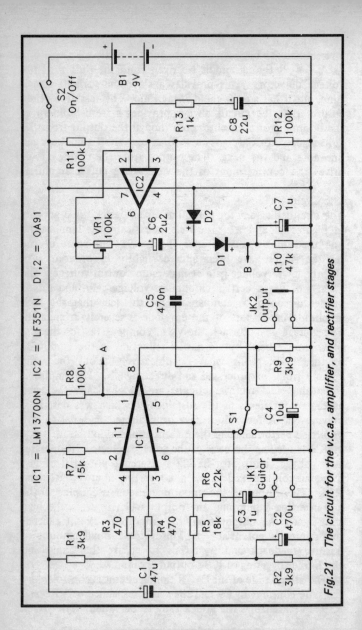

Fig.21 The circuit for the v.c.a., amplifier, and rectifier stages

50

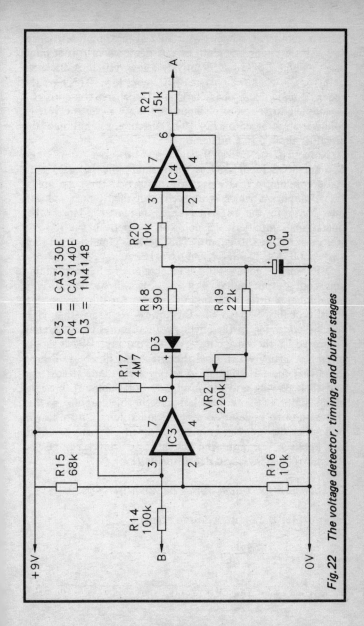

Fig.22 The voltage detector, timing, and buffer stages

IC3 = CA3130E
IC4 = CA3140E
D3 = 1N4148

51

time is about two seconds with VR2 at maximum resistance, and a little under one-tenth of this figure when it is at minimum value. D3 and R18 provide a low resistance discharge path for C9 when the output of IC3 goes low. This gives the required rapid decay characteristic. The charge voltage on C9 is coupled to the control input of the v.c.a. via the voltage follower stage based on IC4. The current consumption of the circuit is about 5 to 6 milliamps.

Note that the CA3130E and CA3140E used for IC3 and IC4 are MOS input devices that require the standard antistatic handling precautions. Also note that these are operational amplifiers which work well with their inputs and outputs close to the negative supply potential. Most other operational amplifiers will not work properly in the IC3 and IC4 positions of this circuit. This includes popular types such as the LF351N, TL081CP, and μA741C.

VR1 enables good results to be obtained with low, medium, and high output guitar pick-ups. It will be necessary to experiment a little with various settings for this component. It is probably best to use the lowest resistance that gives reliable triggering of the circuit, without notes being severely truncated by the v.c.a. cutting off too quickly. VR2 is simply given the setting which gives the effect you like best. Bear in mind that there is no point in setting a very long attack time and then playing notes in machine-gun fashion. With a long attack time each note must last a reasonable duration, so that it has time to build-up to a significant volume. Also bear in mind that the unit can only work properly if there is a small gap between one note and the next. Highly accomplished "seamless" playing might defeat the unit!

Components for Guitar Envelope Modifier (Figs 21 & 22)

Resistors (all 0.25 watt 5% carbon film)

R1	3k9
R2	3k9
R3	470R
R4	470R
R5	18k
R6	22k

R7	15k
R8	100k
R9	3k9
R10	47k
R11	100k
R12	100k
R13	1k
R14	100k
R15	68k
R16	10k
R17	4M7
R18	390R
R19	22k
R20	10k
R21	15k

Potentiometers

VR1	100k min preset
VR2	220k lin carbon

Capacitors

C1	47µ 16V elect
C2	470µ 10V elect
C3	1µ 50V elect
C4	10µ 25V elect
C5	470n polyester
C6	2µ2 50V elect
C7	1µ 50V elect
C8	22µ 25V elect
C9	10µ 25V elect

Semiconductors

IC1	LM13700N or LM13600N
IC2	LF351N
IC3	CA3130E
IC4	CA3140E
D1	OA91
D2	OA91
D3	1N4148

Miscellaneous

S1	SPDT heavy duty push-button
S2	SPST min toggle
JK1	Standard 6.35mm jack socket
JK2	Standard 6.35mm jack socket
B1	9 volt (PP3 size)
	Battery connector
	8 pin DIL IC holder (3 off)
	16 pin DIL IC holder
	Control knob
	Metal case
	Circuit board, wire, solder, etc.

10. Waa-Waa Pedal

The waa-waa effect is not exactly a recent addition to the guitarist's range of effects units, and it must actually be one of the earliest of musical effects. It remains an excellent effect though, and it is certainly one that has remained popular with guitarists over the years. The waa-waa effect is produced by filtering, and a waa-waa unit is basically just a bandpass filter. In other words, a narrow band of frequencies can pass through to the output of the unit unattenuated, but frequencies above and below this band are attenuated.

In order to produce the waa-waa effect it is essential that the centre frequency of the filter is swept up and down over the low and middle audio range. This sweeping of the filter is conventionally controlled via a pedal, but it can be controlled automatically if preferred. This effect is probably at its best with skilful manual control of the filtering, but dynamic control of the filter provides quite a good effect. The waa-waa name of this effect is simply derived from the "waa-waa" sound it produces when applied to a signal that contains a wide range of frequencies (which includes the output from an electric guitar).

Figure 23 shows the circuit diagram for the waa-waa unit. IC1a simply acts as a buffer stage ahead of the tunable bandpass filter. The latter is a conventional operational amplifier

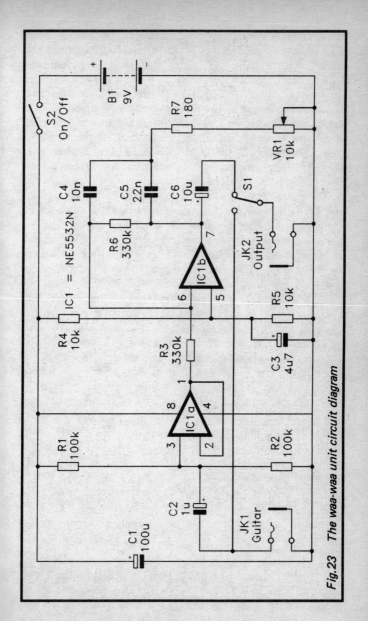

Fig.23   The waa-waa unit circuit diagram

55

bandpass filter configuration which is made tunable by having a variable resistance (VR1) as one element of the filter network. This enables the centre frequency to be adjusted between about 50Hz and 2.8kHz. A slight drawback of this very simple filter configuration is that the Q of the filter varies with changes in the filter's operating frequency. It is significantly higher with VR1 set towards minimum resistance, than with it set at maximum resistance. As the filter frequency is increased, the Q of the circuit therefore increases as well. In practice this does not seem to prevent a good effect from being obtained though.

The overall Q of the circuit is governed by the value of R3 and R6 (which should have the same value). Using a higher value gives a higher Q value and a stronger effect. Using a lower value has the opposite effect. The Q of the circuit can be made adjustable by using a dual gang 470k variable resistor for R3 and R6. However, the suggested value for R3 and R6 is a good compromise that will provide excellent results. A lower value tends to give inadequate Q at low frequencies, and a weak effect. A higher value gives excessive Q at high frequencies, and too strong an effect.

The NE5532N used for IC1 is a dual very low noise bipolar operational amplifier. This ensures good results with a low noise level even if the unit is used with a very low output guitar pick-up. If the unit is used with high output pick-ups the noise performance of IC1 will be of lesser importance, and an LF353N or similar Bifet dual operational amplifier should then be perfectly adequate. The current consumption of the circuit is about 7.5 milliamps, and a PP3 size battery is just about adequate to supply this. It would be advisable to use a higher capacity nine volt battery if the unit is likely to be used extensively. Incidentally, the current consumption is reduced to about 3.5 milliamps if a dual Bifet device is used for IC1.

As far as the electronics are concerned, construction of this project is very simple indeed. The mechanical side of things is rather more awkward. Unless you can play using one hand it is necessary to construct a pedal mechanism so the VR1 can be operated by foot! One way around the problem is to build the unit into a swell pedal, which will have a pedal mechanism controlling a potentiometer. The potentiometer may have the wrong value, and will be a logarithmic type not a linear potentiometer, so it will have to be removed and replaced with a 10k linear type.

If you decide to make your own pedal unit it is certainly possible to use a rotary potentiometer, but I have always found it difficult to obtain reliable operation using a pedal based on a rotary potentiometer. I have found it easier to base home-made pedal units on a slider potentiometer using the basic scheme of things outlined in Figure 24. If you use this method it is a good idea to use a logarithmic potentiometer for VR1. A better control characteristic is obtained using a logarithmic potentiometer upside-down so as to effectively obtain anti-log operation. Of course, the same trick can be used with a rotary potentiometer, provided the pedal mechanism drives it "backwards". It is the convention with waa-waa pedals that pressing the pedal downwards increases the operating frequency of the filter. The unit would probably be very awkward to use if the pedal operated with the opposite sense.

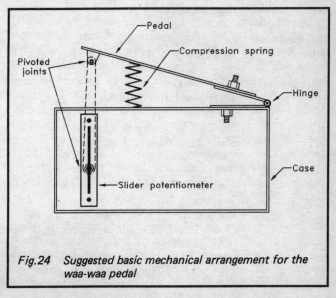

Fig.24   Suggested basic mechanical arrangement for the waa-waa pedal

Components for Waa-Waa Pedal (Fig.23)

Resistors (all 0.25 watt 5% carbon film)
R1	100k
R2	100k
R3	330k
R4	10k
R5	10k
R6	330k
R7	180R

Potentiometer
VR1	10k lin carbon (see text)

Capacitors
C1	100μ 10V elect
C2	1μ 50V elect
C3	4μ7 50V elect
C4	10n polyester
C5	22n polyester
C6	10μ 25V elect

Semiconductor
IC1	NE5532N or LF353N

Miscellaneous
S1	SPDT heavy duty push-button
S2	SPST min toggle
JK1	Standard 6.35mm jack socket
JK2	Standard 6.35mm jack socket
B1	9 volt (PP3 size)
	Battery connector
	8 pin DIL IC holder
	Metal case
	Materials for pedal mechanism
	Circuit board, wire, solder, etc.

11. Improved Waa-Waa

The circuit diagram of Figure 25 is for an improved waa-waa
pedal based on an LM13700N dual transconductance amplifier. This is connected in the transconductance amplifier
version of a state variable filter. A bandpass response is
available at the output of IC1a, and it is this response that is
needed for a conventional waa-waa effect. A lowpass response
is available at the output of IC1b, and this will also give quite
a good waa-waa effect. Although this response is a lowpass
type, it has a pronounced peak just below the cutoff
frequency.

Figure 26 shows a conventional bandpass response (top)
and the type of response obtained at the output of IC1b
(bottom). Both responses enable the fundamental frequency
or a harmonic to be boosted, and give a form of waa-waa
effect. The difference is that when the bandpass response is
used to boost a harmonic, it also attenuates the fundamental
frequency and any lower frequency harmonics. The peaked
lowpass response leaves the fundamental signal and any lower
frequency harmonics unaffected, which produces a slightly
weaker effect. You might like to try using the lowpass output to see if you prefer this version of the waa-waa effect.

The Q of the filter is controlled by VR1. The higher the
value of VR1, the more pronounced the peak in the frequency
response becomes, and the stronger the effect that is obtained.
VR1 gives a very wide control range. When it is at minimum
value the Q of the filter is very low, and the effect obtained
is very weak. With it at maximum value the Q of the filter
is very high, and the effect produced is too strong for most
tastes. It is worthwhile spending some time trying VR1 at
various settings, but the best effect will probably be obtained
with it set at around half maximum resistance, or a little less.

As it is based on transconductance amplifiers, the circuit is
current controlled. However, R11 and VR2 are placed in
series with the control inputs of IC1, and these effectively
give voltage controlled operation. VR3 provides the control
voltage, and is the potentiometer in the pedal mechanism.
VR2 controls the range of frequencies covered by VR3.
Using a high value for VR2 gives a very low minimum filter

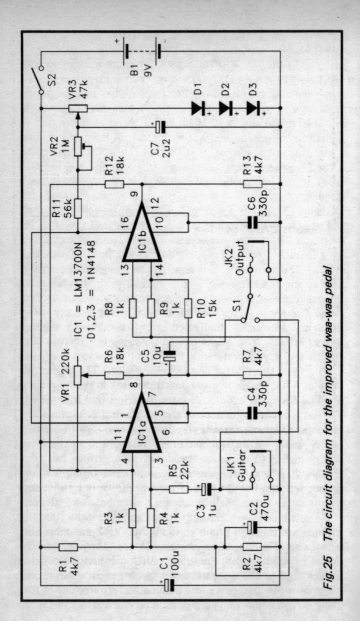

Fig.25 The circuit diagram for the improved waa-waa pedal

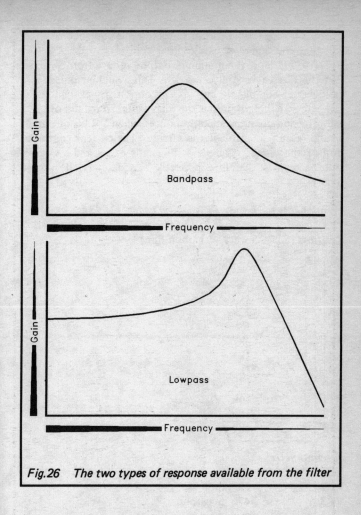

Fig.26   The two types of response available from the filter

frequency, and also produces a relatively low maximum filter frequency. Using a low value gives a higher minimum frequency, although the filter can still be tuned quite low in frequency.   At the other end of the range it permits the filter's centre frequency to be taken well up towards the top end of the audio range. Setting up VR2 correctly is just a matter of using trial and error to achieve the control characteristic that you find most easy to use.

D1 to D3 limit the minimum output voltage from VR3, so that the filter never fully cuts off. This would be undesirable as it would completely cut off the output signal, and could generate switching noises as the filter switched on and off. C7 smooths out any noise spikes produced when VR3 is operated, giving "silent" control of the circuit. The current consumption of the circuit is about 4 milliamps or so, and a small 9 volt battery is therefore perfectly adequate as the power source.

Components for Improved Waa-Waa Pedal (Fig.25)

Resistors (all 0.25 watt 5% carbon film)
R1	4k7
R2	4k7
R3	1k
R4	1k
R5	22k
R6	18k
R7	4k7
R8	1k
R9	1k
R10	15k
R11	56k
R12	18k
R13	4k7

Potentiometers
VR1	220k lin carbon
VR2	1M min preset
VR3	47k lin carbon

Capacitors
C1	100μ 10V elect
C2	470μ 10V elect
C3	1μ 50V elect
C4	330p polystyrene
C5	10μ 25V elect

| C6 | 330p polystyrene |
| C7 | 2µ2 50V elect |

Semiconductors
IC1	LM13700N or LM13600N
D1	1N4148
D2	1N4148
D3	1N4148

Miscellaneous
S1	SPDT heavy duty push-button
S2	SPST min toggle
JK1	Standard 6.35mm jack socket
JK2	Standard 6.35mm jack socket
B1	9 volt (PP3 size)
	Battery connector
	16 pin DIL IC holder
	Control knob
	Metal case
	Materials for pedal mechanism
	Circuit board, wire, solder, etc.

12. Auto-Waa

Automatic operation of a waa-waa unit has a definite advantage for the home constructor. Not least of these is the fact that it avoids the need to construct a pedal mechanism. There are two general approaches to automatic control of this effect. One is to simply have the filter controlled by a low frequency oscillator, in basically the same manner that the tremolo effect is controlled. To my ears at any rate, this method does not give particularly good results. The waa-waa effect is at its best with the filter controlled in a rather more subtle way.

It is unlikely that any form of automatic operation will genuinely give results that rival those obtained from a waa-waa pedal operated by a talented musician, but the second approach at least comes that bit closer. This second method is to have the filter frequency under dynamic control. In other

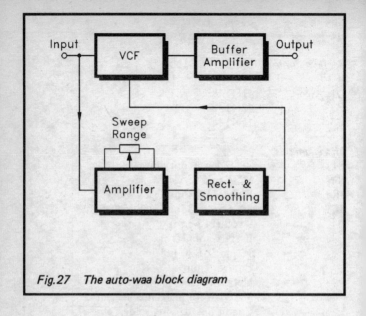

Fig.27 The auto-waa block diagram

words, the higher the amplitude of the input signal, the higher the centre frequency of the filter. This gives a good effect, and one that has real musical possibilities. Due to the fast attack and slow decay of a guitar, the "waa" sound produced as the filter frequency is swept upwards at the beginning of a note is so brief as to be virtually non-existent. The effect is largely produced as the filter frequency falls back as each note decays. It is perhaps more accurately described as a "waa" effect than a true waa-waa type.

Figure 27 shows the block diagram for the automatic waa unit. A voltage controlled bandpass filter and a buffer amplifier are used in the main signal path. The control voltage for the v.c.f. is produced by first amplifying part of the input signal. The amplified signal is then rectified and smoothed to produce a positive d.c. signal that is fed to the control input of the v.c.f. This voltage is roughly proportional to the amplitude of the input signal, and it therefore varies the filter's centre frequency in sympathy with changes

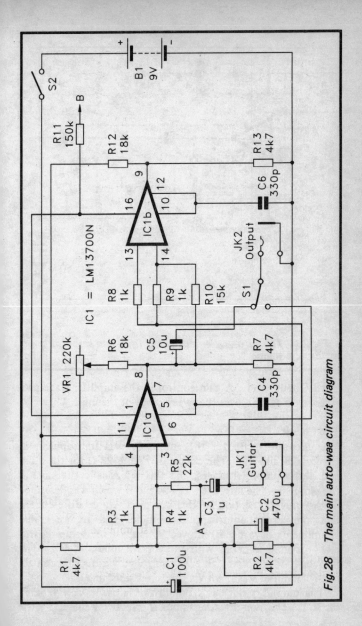

Fig.28 The main auto-waa circuit diagram

65

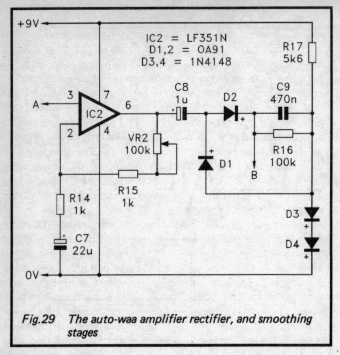

Fig.29   The auto-waa amplifier rectifier, and smoothing stages

in the input level. A gain control in the amplifier stage provides some control over the sweep range of the unit.

The Circuit
The circuit diagram for the automatic waa unit appears in Figures 28 and 29. The circuit of Figure 28 is for the v.c.f. and buffer amplifier stages, and this is basically the same as the circuit for the improved waa-waa unit which was described in the previous section of this book. The only difference is that the sweep control potentiometer and its associated components have been removed. Also, a fixed value resistor (R11) is used in series with the control inputs of IC1. The frequency range of the filter is controlled via the gain control of the amplifier stage, not via this series resistance.

The amplifier stage is a non-inverting mode circuit based on IC2. The non-inverting input is effectively biased by the

66

bias circuit of IC1, due to the direct coupling to the input of the v.c.f. VR2 enables IC2's closed loop voltage gain to be varied between unity and just over 100 times (40dB). This gives good control over the upper limit of the filter's sweep range, and it also enables the unit to operate well with any normal guitar pick-ups. A conventional half-wave rectifier circuit is used. Germanium rather than silicon diodes are used in this circuit because their lower forward voltage drops give a better control characteristic. R17, D3, and D4 provide a potential of about 1.3 volts, and the output of the smoothing circuit is referenced to this, not to the 0 volt supply rail. This ensures that the filter does not cut off under quiescent conditions. The attack and decay times of the smoothing circuit are both quite short, which ensures that the unit accurately tracks the changing input level.

As the circuit consumes about 6 milliamps a PP3 size battery is adequate as the power source. However, it might be worthwhile to use a higher capacity battery if the unit is likely to be used frequently and for long periods. Experiment a little with settings for VR2. The effect is probably best with VR2 set just high enough to give a reasonably wide sweep range. However, it is obviously quite in order to use any setting that you feel provides a good effect. If the unit is used with low output pick-ups it might be found that VR2 has to be set well towards maximum resistance before the filter frequency is swept over a reasonably wide range. Adding a resistor of about 56k in series with VR2 should give improved results. Reducing R11 to 100k might also give better results.

Components for Auto-Waa (Figs 28 & 29)

Resistors (all 0.25 watt 5% carbon film)

R1	4k7
R2	4k7
R3	1k
R4	1k
R5	22k
R6	18k
R7	4k7

R8	1k
R9	1k
R10	15k
R11	150k
R12	18k
R13	4k7
R14	1k
R15	1k
R16	100k
R17	5k6

Potentiometers

VR1	220k lin carbon
VR2	100k lin carbon

Capacitors

C1	100μ 10V elect
C2	470μ 10V elect
C3	1μ 50V elect
C4	330p polystyrene
C5	10μ 25V elect
C6	330p polystyrene
C7	22μ 50V elect
C8	1μ 50V elect
C9	470n polyester

Semiconductors

IC1	LM13700N or LM13600N
IC2	LF351N
D1	OA91
D2	OA91
D3	1N4148
D4	1N4148

Miscellaneous

S1	SPDT heavy duty push-button
S2	SPST min toggle
JK1	Standard 6.35mm jack socket
JK2	Standard 6.35mm jack socket
B1	9 volt (PP3 size)

Battery connector
16 pin DIL IC holder
8 pin DIL IC holder
Control knob (2 off)
Metal case
Circuit board, wire, solder, etc.

13. Tremolo Unit

This is another effect which is definitely in the "golden oldie" category. It is produced using a low frequency oscillator to amplitude modulate the input signal. The waveform diagram

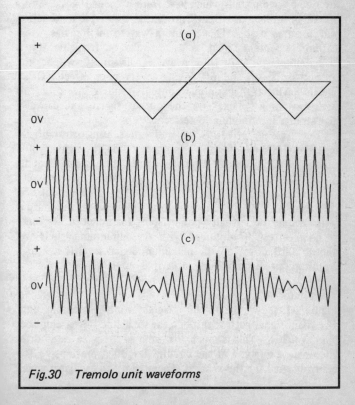

Fig.30   Tremolo unit waveforms

69

of Figure 30 helps to explain the way in which this simple process operates. Waveform (a) is the low frequency modulation signal, and waveform (b) is the input signal at a much higher frequency. When the modulation signal is at its peak voltage, the output signal is at full strength. As the modulation voltage falls back from its peak value the output level is gradually reduced. The output is reduced to virtually zero when the modulation signal reaches its minimum value. The amplitude of the output signal therefore varies at a rate which is controlled by the frequency of the low frequency oscillator. Rapidly operating a swell pedal actually gives the same effect, but is obviously not a very practical means of generating this effect.

Although the tremolo effect is basically very simple, there are one or two pitfalls which have to be avoided if good results are to be obtained. It is essential that a suitable modulation waveform is used. This means a waveform that has a low harmonic content, such as a sinewave or triangular type. Using simple pulse or squarewave signals simply switches the output signal on and off, giving a very poor effect. Other signals having high harmonic contents tend to give problems with switching "clicks" on the output signal, and can also give strange intermodulation effects.

The tremolo effect is generally best using substantially less than 100% modulation. In other words, the signal should not be totally cut off when the modulation signal is at its minimum potential. With full modulation an excessive throbbing effect tends to be produced at high modulation frequencies. At low modulation frequencies the output signal would be virtually non-existent for much of the time! A good effect is produced with the minimum signal level about 20dB down on the maximum signal level (i.e. a high amplitude to low amplitude ratio of about 10 to 1).

The Circuit
Figure 31 shows the circuit diagram for the tremolo unit. The main signal path is through the v.c.a. and buffer amplifier based on IC1. This is much the same as the v.c.a. and buffer circuit used in some of the circuits described previously. The control signal for the v.c.a. is generated by an oscillator which

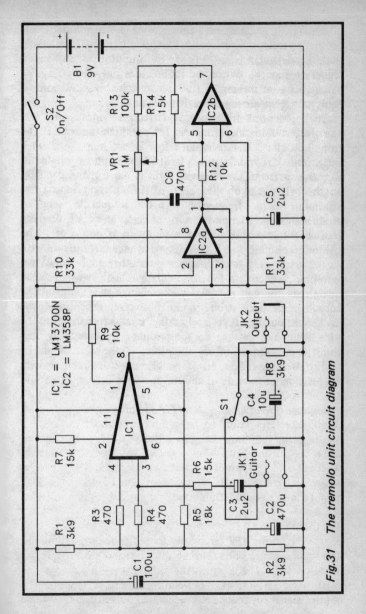

Fig.31   The tremolo unit circuit diagram

71

is based on IC2. This uses a conventional configuration which has IC2a as an integrator and IC2b as a trigger circuit. This gives a triangular waveform at the output of IC2a, and a squarewave at the output of IC2b. It is only the triangular signal that is of interest in this case, and it drives the control input of IC1 via series resistor R9.

The oscillator's frequency is variable by means of VR1. The output frequency range is from a little under 1Hz to around 10Hz. The tremolo effect is not very good with extremely low modulation frequencies, and a minimum modulation frequency of about 1Hz is more than adequate. At the other end of the range, 10Hz represents about the maximum usable frequency. Higher frequencies tend to produce unwanted modulation effects, and can produce audible breakthrough from the modulation oscillator. The LM358P specified for IC2 is a type which can operate with its output at very low voltages. Most other dual operational amplifiers will either fail to oscillate reliably when used in this circuit, or will not give a low enough minimum output voltage to produce strong modulation. One exception is the CA3240E, but this is generally rather more expensive than the LM358P. The current consumption of the circuit is only about 4 milliamps. In use the effect of the unit should be fairly obvious. The effect is generally at its best with modulation frequencies of about 3 to 10Hz.

Components for Tremolo Unit (Fig.31)

Resistors (all 0.25 watt 5% carbon film)

R1	3k9
R2	3k9
R3	470R
R4	470R
R5	18k
R6	15k
R7	15k
R8	3k9
R9	10k
R10	33k
R11	33k

R12	10k
R13	100k
R14	15k

Potentiometer
| VR1 | 1M lin carbon |

Capacitors
C1	100μ 10V elect
C2	470μ 10V elect
C3	2μ2 50V elect
C4	10μ 25V elect
C5	2μ2 50V elect
C6	470n polyester

Semiconductors
| IC1 | LM13700N or LM13600N |
| IC2 | LM358P |

Miscellaneous
S1	SPDT heavy-duty push-button
S2	SPST min toggle
JK1	Standard 6.35mm jack socket
JK2	Standard 6.35mm jack socket
B1	9 volt (PP3 size)
	Battery connector
	16 pin DIL IC holder
	8 pin DIL IC holder
	Control knob
·	Metal case
	Circuit board, wire, solder, etc.

14. Split Phase Tremolo

A split phase tremolo unit is a form of stereo tremolo unit. However, it has the two stereo channels modulated in anti-phase fashion. The waveforms of Figure 32 show the effect of a split phase tremolo unit. Waveform (a) is the output from

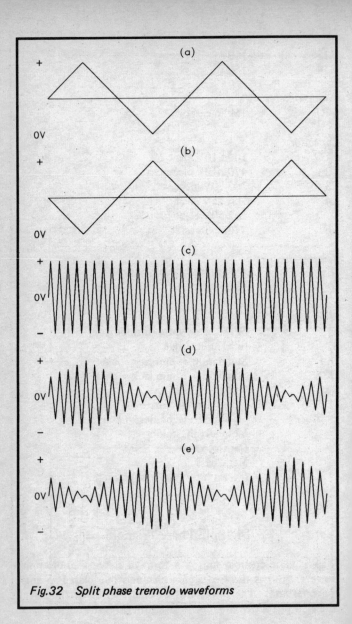

Fig.32   Split phase tremolo waveforms

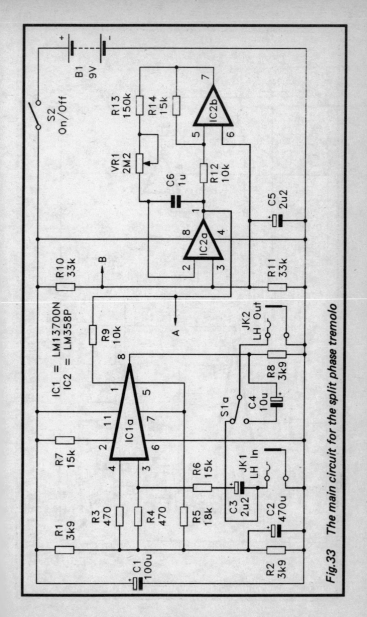

Fig.33 The main circuit for the split phase tremolo

75

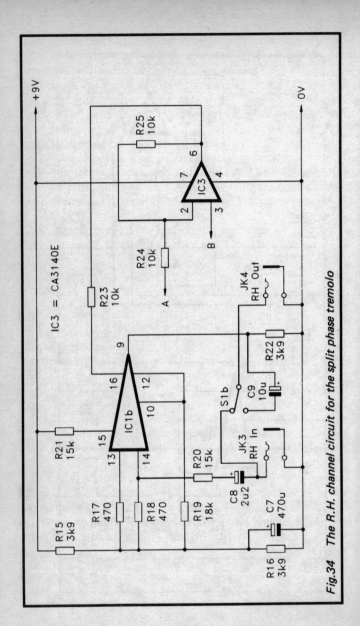

Fig.34 The R.H. channel circuit for the split phase tremolo

76

the low frequency modulation oscillator, and waveform (b) is the anti-phase signal that is generated from this. Waveform (c) is the input signal to both channels of the unit. Waveforms (d) and (e) are the stereo outputs. Both are low frequency modulated, but when (d) is at maximum amplitude (e) is at its minimum level. Similarly, when (e) is at its peak level, (d) is at its minimum amplitude.

One way of using a split phase tremolo unit is to have different instruments connected to each stereo input. This can give quite a good effect, but probably the most common way of using a unit of this type is to feed one instrument to both inputs. It then has the effect of panning that instrument from side-to-side in the stereo sound stage.

Figures 33 and 34 show the circuit diagram for the split phase tremolo unit. Figure 33 has obvious similarities to the tremolo circuit described previously (Figure 31). It really only differs from this in that the values of the timing components in the low frequency oscillator have been altered. Unlike the ordinary tremolo effect, the split phase variety does not give a good effect with fairly high modulation frequencies. Rapid panning of a signal across a stereo sound stage gives what many find to be a slightly nauseating experience, particularly when using headphones. It is advisable to use slower modulation frequencies with the split phase tremolo effect, and the oscillator has therefore been modified to give a somewhat lower frequency range. The actual frequency range is from about 0.25Hz (one cycle every four seconds) to 3Hz.

The other channel of the unit utilizes the other section of IC1 in an identical v.c.a. circuit. This is driven from the low frequency oscillator via IC3, which simply acts as a unity voltage gain inverting amplifier. It therefore provides the required anti-phase modulation. The current consumption of the circuit is about 8 milliamps or so. A PP3 size battery is just about adequate to provide this, but it would be advisable to use a higher capacity battery unless the unit will only receive light use.

Components for Split Phase Tremolo (Figs 33 & 34)

Resistors (all 0.25 watt 5% carbon film)

R1	3k9
R2	3k9
R3	470R
R4	470R
R5	18k
R6	15k
R7	15k
R8	3k9
R9	10k
R10	33k
R11	33k
R12	10k
R13	150k
R14	15k
R15	3k9
R16	3k9
R17	470R
R18	470R
R19	18k
R20	15k
R21	15k
R22	3k9
R23	10k
R24	10k
R25	10k

Potentiometer

VR1	2M2 lin carbon

Capacitors

C1	100μ 10V elect
C2	470μ 10V elect
C3	2μ2 50V elect
C4	10μ 25V elect
C5	2μ2 50V elect
C6	1μ polyester
C7	470μ 10V elect

| C8 | 2μ2 50V elect |
| C9 | 10μ 25V elect |

Semiconductors

IC1	LM13700N or LM13600N
IC2	LM358P
IC3	CA3140E

Miscellaneous

S1	DPDT heavy duty push-button
S2	SPST min toggle
JK1 to JK4	Standard 6.35mm jack socket (4 off)
B1	9 volt (PP3 size)
	Battery connector
	16 pin DIL IC holder
	8 pin DIL IC holder (2 off)
	Control knob
	Metal case
	Circuit board, wire, solder, etc.

15. Phaser

The name of this effect is derived from the way it is generated, and not because it alters the phase of the processed signal. It is really a form of filter effect. A phaser produces one or more "notches" of deep attenuation in the frequency response of the system. In other words, it produces a high degree of attenuation, but only over a very narrow band (or bands). A phaser also produces peaks of increased gain in the frequency response, but these are really just a byproduct of the way in which the effect is produced. These peaks do not alter the effect to a significant degree because they are too broad, and provide no more than a 6dB boost in gain.

The notches are swept up and down the audio range at a slow rate (usually around 1Hz). A single notch produces a worthwhile effect, but much better results are obtained with twin notches. The effect can be further improved by using

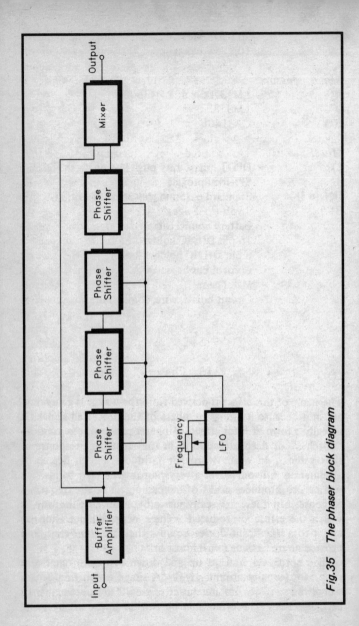

Fig.35 The phaser block diagram

more notches, but with each additional notch the improvement is that much less obvious, and the complexity of the unit grows rapidly. The phaser feature here has twin notches, but it is easily modified to have three or more notches. It can also be simplified to have a single notch if desired.

System Operation

Figure 35 shows the block diagram for the phaser effects unit. The input signal is fed to a buffer amplifier, and then through a series of four phase shifters. The phase shifters are voltage controlled, and provide a phase shift that varies between zero and 720 degrees. The phase obtained is frequency dependent, and the higher the input frequency, the higher the phase shift. The 720 degree maximum can never be exceeded though, no matter how high the input frequency is taken. The phase shift is also dependent on the control voltage, and the frequency at which a given phase shift is obtained can therefore be altered via the control voltage.

The important phase shifts in this application are 180 degrees and 540 degrees (360 degrees plus 180 degrees). In both cases the output from the final phase shifter is out-of-phase with the input signal. The output from the final phase shifter is mixed with the output from the buffer amplifier. At frequencies where the two signals are in-phase, they add together to produce a boost in the output signal. The waveforms of Figure 36 help to explain this process. The waveforms of (a) and (b) are in-phase input signals. As one would probably expect, adding these together in a mixer gives an output signal having double the amplitude of the two input signals.

What is of greater interest is the effect of mixing two signals that are identical, but 180 degrees out-of-phase (waveforms (d) and (e)). A positive voltage in one waveform is matched by an equal negative voltage in the other waveform, and vice versa. Mixing these two signals together therefore produces zero output (waveform (f)). Mixing the phase shifted signal with the unprocessed input signal therefore produces deep notches in the frequency response at the two frequencies where the two signals are out-of-phase. The low frequency oscillator sweeps these notches up and down the audio range,

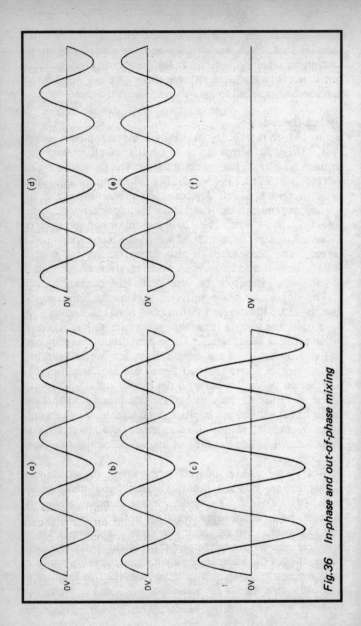

Fig.36 In-phase and out-of-phase mixing

generating the phasing effect.

If only a single notch is required, this can be achieved by using just two phase shifters instead of four. This gives a phase shift of between zero and 360 degrees, with the single notch at the frequency where a 180 degree phase shift is produced. The circuit produces one notch per pair of phase shifters. If you require (say) four notches, it is just a matter of using a chain of eight phase shifters in the unit.

The Circuit

The circuit diagram for the phaser effects unit appears in Figures 37, 38, and 39. Taking Figure 37 first, IC1 acts as the input buffer stage, and it gives the unit an input impedance of about 50k. IC2 is the mixer stage, and this is a conventional operational amplifier summing mode circuit. This is a modified form of inverting amplifier which has an extra input resistor for each additional input.

In order to obtain deep notches it is necessary for the two input signals to be at the same amplitude, or something close to it. In practice I have never found it necessary to have the input signals very accurately balanced in order to obtain a good phasing effect. However, if preferred, R4 can be replaced by an 18k fixed resistor in series with a 10k preset resistor. The preset resistor can then be adjusted to optimise the effect. The circuit was found to be slightly unstable, and occasionally broke into high frequency oscillation. This was cured by using C5 to provide a small amount of high frequency roll-off. This only affects frequencies outside the audio range incidentally, and does not impair the audio performance of the circuit.

Figure 38 is the circuit for the chain of four phase shifters. R8, R9, and C7 provides a bias potential of half the supply voltage to all four stages. The four phase shift circuits are essentially the same, and they are based on the standard operational amplifier phase shifter configuration. The circuit is basically a unity voltage gain inverting amplifier. However, the capacitive coupling from the input to the non-inverting input produces a decreasing amount of phase shift as the input frequency is raised, and the reactance of the capacitor reduces. In effect, the circuit gradually changes from an

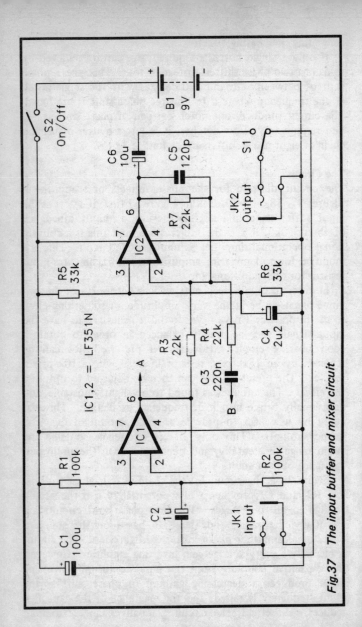

Fig.37 The input buffer and mixer circuit

84

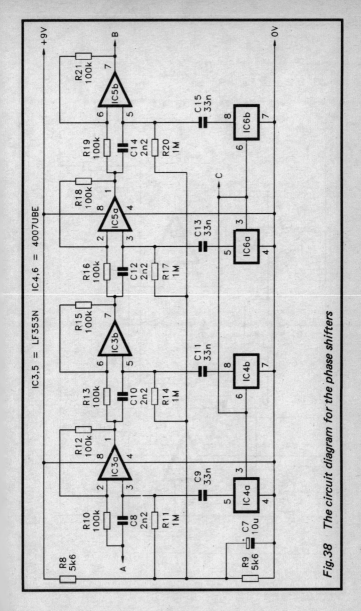

Fig.38   The circuit diagram for the phase shifters

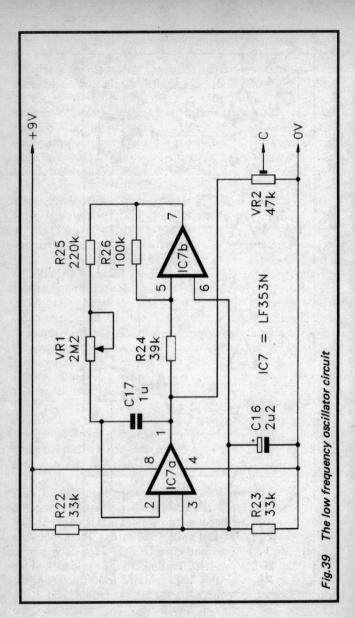

Fig.39 The low frequency oscillator circuit

86

inverting amplifier to a non-inverting type as the input frequency is raised.

A voltage controlled resistance connected between the non-inverting input of each amplifier and the earth rail enables the degree of phase shift at a given frequency to be varied. The four voltage controlled resistors are actually N channel enhancement mode MOSFETs in two CMOS 4007UBE integrated circuits. This device is actually a complementary pair and inverter, but it is useful for voltage controlled audio applications as it has two N channel devices that are readily accessible.

If you only require a single notch phaser, simply omit IC5, IC6, plus the six resistors and four capacitors associated with them. The input of the mixer stage (point "B") is then driven from pin 7 of IC3. If more notches are required, you must add further pairs of phase shifters into the signal path. These can all use R8, R9, and C7 for biasing. I would not recommend going beyond eight phase shifters (four notches). To do so would make the unit quite complex and expensive. It is unlikely that the effect produced and the general audio quality obtained would justify the cost and effort involved.

Figure 39 shows the circuit diagram for the low frequency oscillator. This is basically the same as the equivalent stage in the tremolo unit which was described previously. In this case the output frequency can be adjusted from about 3Hz to 0.33Hz. VR2 is adjusted to give an output voltage range that matches the requirements of the voltage controlled resistors. The total current consumption of the circuit is about 14 milliamps. It is therefore necessary to use a fairly high capacity battery, such as six HP7 (AA) size cells in a plastic holder.

When constructing this unit, remember that the 4007UBE used for IC4 and IC6 is a CMOS device, and that it requires the usual anti-static handling precautions. This device should have a "UBE" suffix, and not a "BE" suffix. There should be no problem here, since most component retailers only seem to supply the "UBE" version. Try to keep the oscillator and the wiring to VR1 reasonably well separated from the rest of the circuit and wiring. There is a squarewave output from IC7b, and this can couple switching "clicks" into the main signal

87

path if a careless layout is used.

VR2 is given any setting that provides a wide sweep range. When setting up and testing the unit it is a good idea to use some form of noise source as the input signal. If a v.h.f. radio is tuned between stations, a good noise signal can be obtained from the earphone socket. On a signal such as this, which contains a wide range of frequencies, the effect should be very obvious indeed. You should be able to hear the notches being swept up and down in frequency. Set VR1 for a low frequency so that the effect of the unit is easy to follow, and then try VR2 at various settings. Best results will be obtained using a setting that sweeps the notches well down towards the low frequency end of the audio range. The filtering should always be "on the move". Avoid settings which take the filtering to one or other extreme of the audio range, let it hang there momentarily, and then move on again.

When using any phaser effects unit it must be borne in mind that it will only produce a good effect on an input signal that contains a wide range of frequencies. It therefore gives a better effect with a guitar signal that has been "fuzzed" or treble boosted, than it does with the "straight" output from a guitar. It works well with a synthesiser set to give pulse or noise based sounds.

Components for Phaser Effects Unit (Figs 37, 38 & 39)

Resistors (all 0.25 watt 5% carbon film)

R1	100k
R2	100k
R3	22k
R4	22k
R5	33k
R6	33k
R7	22k
R8	5k6
R9	5k6
R10	100k
R11	1M
R12	100k
R13	100k

R14	1M
R15	100k
R16	100k
R17	1M
R18	100k
R19	100k
R20	1M
R21	100k
R22	33k
R23	33k
R24	39k
R25	220k
R26	100k

Potentiometers

VR1	2M2 lin carbon
VR2	47k min preset

Capacitors

C1	100μ 10V elect
C2	1μ 50V elect
C3	220n polyester
C4	$2\mu2$ 50V elect
C5	120p polystyrene
C6	10μ 25V elect
C7	10μ 25V elect
C8	2n2 polyester
C9	33n polyester
C10	2n2 polyester
C11	33n polyester
C12	2n2 polyester
C13	33n polyester
C14	2n2 polyester
C15	33n polyester
C16	$2\mu2$ 50V elect
C17	1μ polyester

Semiconductors

IC1	LF351N
IC2	LF351N

IC3	LF353N
IC4	4007UBE
IC5	LF353N
IC6	4007UBE
IC7	LF353N

Miscellaneous

S1	DPDT heavy duty push-button
S2	SPST min toggle
JK1	Standard 6.35mm jack socket
JK2	Standard 6.35mm jack socket
B1	9 volt (6 × HP7 size cells)
	Battery holder
	Battery connector (PP3 size)
	14 pin DIL IC holder (2 off)
	8 pin DIL IC holder (5 off)
	Control knob
	Metal case
	Circuit board, wire, solder, etc.

16. Metal Effects Unit

Metal effects have a reputation for being rather extreme, probably due to their "heavy metal" connections. In reality a metal effect can be so mild as to be barely discernable, so strong that it is totally discordant, or anywhere between these two extremes. Just why does a metal effect produce strong discord if it is taken to extremes?

Most western instruments have a simple resonator such as a string or tube, which is essential one-dimensional. When vibrated this produces a fundamental frequency, plus harmonics (multiples of the fundamental frequency). Most effects units add harmonics, or alter the relative strengths of the harmonics that are already present, but maintain the same basic scheme of things, with a fundamental plus some harmonics.

A metal effects unit generates frequencies that are not harmonically related to the input frequency. The output from an oscillator in the effects unit is heterodyned with the input signal to produce sum and difference frequencies. For example, suppose that the input signal is at a frequency of 440Hz (middle A), and that the oscillator is operating at 20Hz. By heterodyning these two signals output frequencies at 460H (440Hz + 20Hz) and 420Hz (440Hz − 20Hz) are produced. A metal effects unit can generate signals which, although not harmonically related to the input signal, are still notes on the musical scale. However, if a fixed oscillator frequency is used, processing some notes may produce harmonious results, but others will generate strong discord.

The simple way around this problem is to use a low modulation frequency of around 5 to 20Hz, and to generate only relatively weak sum and difference frequencies. This gives melodious results and a very good effect. Using stronger modulation and suppressing the input signal gives what is very definitely a heavy metal style effect. The unit described here can provide both types of effect, or an in-between effect, simply by adjusting the modulation control. Incidentally, the "metal" name is derived from the fact that many instruments that are made from metal produce frequencies that are not harmonically related to the fundamental frequency. Gongs and bells for example, are two- or three-dimensional, and produce a wide range of output frequencies due to their multiple resonances.

The Circuit

Figure 40 shows the circuit diagram for the input and modulator stages. The circuit diagram for the low frequency oscillator appears in Figure 41. Taking the input stage first, this is an operational amplifier non-inverting mode circuit. VR1 enables the closed loop voltage gain to be varied between unity and eleven times. VR1 is set at or close to minimum resistance if the unit is used with a high output guitar. For low and medium output pick-ups it is better to set VR1 for a much higher resistance so that a moderate amount of voltage gain is produced. This ensures that the modulator is fed with a fairly high signal level, which in turn ensures that the main signal is kept well above any slight breakthrough from the modulation oscillator, and the general background noise level.

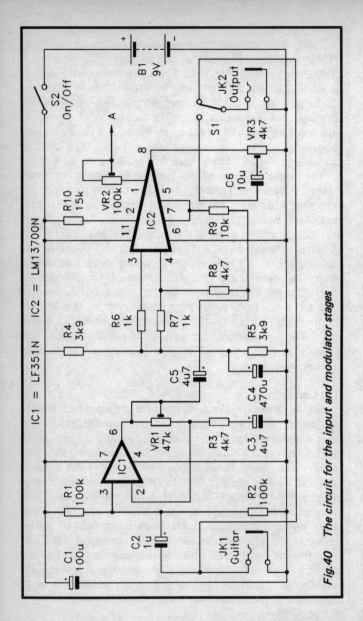

IC1 = LF351N   IC2 = LM13700N

Fig.40 The circuit for the input and modulator stages

92

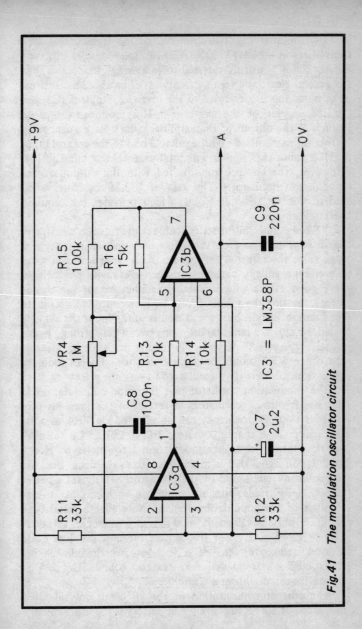

Fig.41   The modulation oscillator circuit

93

The modulator is based on one of the transconductance amplifiers in an LM13700N (IC2). In music circles this type of oscillator is usually referred to as a "ring" modulator, but in general electronic terms it is a form of balanced modulator. The input signal is coupled to the inverting input of IC2, and to the output of the amplifier. This produces anti-phase signals at the output of the amplifier, which have a cancelling effect on each other. With a suitable bias to the control input of IC2 these two signals will totally cancel out one another. However, the control input is fed with the output of the modulation oscillator. The gain of IC2 is therefore varied either side of the null point, which provides the required heterodyning.

VR2 is connected in series with the modulation signal, and has a large influence on the effect obtained. If it is set at a high value the effect is very weak. As it is set lower in value the effect gradually becomes stronger, eventually producing a very good effect which is rather reminescent of the chorus effect. Setting the value of VR2 still lower produces stronger modulation signals, but it also results in the input signal being balanced out to a large extent. This gives a very strong "heavy metal" type effect. If you only require one type of effect or the other, VR2 should be a preset resistor. Use an ordinary potentiometer here if you will need to vary the effect.

The modulation oscillator uses the same configuration as the low frequency oscillators in several of the previous projects. Its output frequency can be adjusted via VR4, and the frequency range is approximately 2Hz to 20Hz. C9 "cleans" up the output at higher modulation frequencies to give a modulation signal that is more like a sinewave signal than the triangular output signal of the oscillator. This gives a better effect, and avoids possible problems with audible breakthrough of the modulation signal. Note that a metal type effect is only obtained at modulation frequencies of about 5Hz or more. At lower frequencies the unit provides quite a good tremolo effect. It is therefore worthwhile making the oscillator's frequency range extend below 5Hz, so that the device can double as a tremolo unit.

The current consumption of the circuit is only about 5 milliamps or so. A PP3 size 9 volt battery is therefore suitable as the power source. VR1 should be given the highest resistance that does not produce clipping and serious distortion on the output signal. VR3 is adjusted to balance the volume levels of the processed and straight-through signals. It is worth spending some time experimenting with various settings for VR2 and VR4 to find the effect you like best. A moderate amount of modulation at a frequency of about 10Hz is a good starting point.

Components for Metal Effects Unit (Figs 40 & 41)

Resistors (all 0.25 watt 5% carbon film)

R1	100k
R2	100k
R3	4k7
R4	3k9
R5	3k9
R6	1k
R7	1k
R8	4k7
R9	10k
R10	15k
R11	33k
R12	33k
R13	10k
R14	10k
R15	100k
R16	15k

Potentiometers

VR1	47k min preset
VR2	100k min preset
VR3	4k7 min preset
VR4	1M lin carbon

Capacitors

C1	100μ 10V elect
C2	1μ 50V elect
C3	4μ7 50V elect
C4	470μ 10V elect
C5	4μ7 50V elect

C6	10μ 25V elect
C7	2μ2 50V elect
C8	100n polyester
C9	220n polyester

Semiconductors
IC1	LF351N
IC2	LM13700N or LM13600N
IC3	LM358P

Miscellaneous
S1	SPDT heavy duty push-button
S2	SPST min toggle
JK1	Standard 6.35mm jack socket
JK2	Standard 6.35mm jack socket
B1	9 volt (PP3 size)
	Battery connector
	16 pin DIL IC holder
	8 pin DIL IC holder (2 off)
	Control knob
	Metal case
	Circuit board, wire, solder, etc.

17. Mains Power Supply

All the projects featured in this book are designed for battery power. If you wish to avoid the expense of replacement batteries, NiCad rechargeable types are probably the best option. These give very low running costs in the medium to long term, and do not compromise portability. The circuits can be powered from a ready-made battery eliminator provided it has a 9 volt output, and it also has a properly smoothed output. Many inexpensive battery eliminators have unregulated outputs which have a high ripple content. These are unsuitable for use with the circuits featured here, as they would produce a strong "hum" content on the output signal.

If you wish to build your own mains power supply unit, Figure 42 shows the circuit diagram for a 9 volt mains power

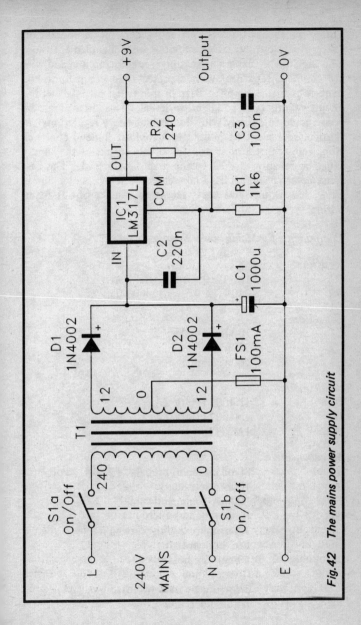

Fig.42   The mains power supply circuit

97

supply which has a low ripple and general noise content on
its regulated output. This circuit is only included for those
who are suitably experienced at project construction, and who
are competent to deal with a project that connects to the
dangerous mains supply. Bear in mind that mistakes with a
circuit of this type could prove lethal. This circuit must be
constructed to comply with the normal safety regulations. In
particular, it must be housed in a case of all-metal construction, and both the case and the 0 volt output of the supply
must be reliably earthed to the mains earth lead. The case
must be a type which has a lid secured by screws, not a clip-on
type that would give easy access to the dangerous mains
wiring.

Components for Mains Power Supply (Fig.42)

Resistors
R1   1k6 1% 0.5 watt metal film
R2   240R 1% 0.5 watt metal film

Capacitors
C1   1000μ 25V elect
C2   220n ceramic
C3   100n ceramic

Semiconductors
D1   1N4002 (100V 1A)
D2   1N4002 (100V 1A)
IC1   LM317L

Miscellaneous
T1   Standard mains primary, 12−0−12 volt
            100mA secondary
FS1   100mA 20mm anti-surge
S1   Rotary mains switch
            All-metal case with screwed lid
            Circuit board
            20mm fuse holder
            Control knob
            3 core mains lead and fused plug (2A)
            Wire, solder, etc.

Notes

Please note following is a list of other titles that are available in our range of Radio, Electronics and Computer books.

These should be available from all good Booksellers, Radio Component Dealers and Mail Order Companies.

However, should you experience difficulty in obtaining any title in your area, then please write directly to the Publisher enclosing payment to cover the cost of the book plus adequate postage.

If you would like a complete catalogue of our entire range of Radio, Electronics and Computer Books then please send a Stamped Addressed Envelope to:

BERNARD BABANI (publishing) LTD
THE GRAMPIANS
SHEPHERDS BUSH ROAD
LONDON W6 7NF
ENGLAND